Nutcracker Sweet

A Family Musical

Book, music and lyrics by

David Wood

Samuel French – London
New York – Sydney – Toronto – Hollywood

NUTCRACKER SWEET

First performed at the Redgrave Theatre, Farnham on 20th December 1977, with the following cast of characters:

Kernel Walnut	Lloyd McGuire
Monkeynut	Christopher Reeks
Gypsy Brazil	Sue Withers
Hazel	Sue Elgin
William the Conker	Peter Corey
Professor Jelly Bon-Bon	Mark Buffery
Old Ma Coconut	Elizabeth Kean

The play directed by David Horlock

Designed by Paul Wright

Musical Director Robert Mitchell

Choreographed by Jonathan Howell

Subsequently presented on tour and at Sadler's Wells Theatre, London, by Whirligig Theatre (sponsored by Clarks Shoes), from August 1980 to January 1981, with the following cast of characters:

Kernel Walnut	Mike Elles
Monkeynut	Robin Wright
Gypsy Brazil	Lucy Fenwick
Hazel	Melody Kaye
William the Conker	Alan Bodenham
Professor Jelly Bon-Bon	Richard Bremmer
Old Ma Coconut	Caroline High

The play directed by David Wood

Designed by Susie Caulcutt

Choreography by Sheila Falconer

Music arranged and supervised by Peter Pontzen

Musical Director Paul Knight

Photographs in this Acting Edition show Susie Caulcutt's designs for the Whirligig Theatre production and were taken by Frazer Ashford.

Characters

Kernel Walnut, a blustery, elderly walnut, who runs the Nutty May Fair

Monkeynut, a combination of nut and monkey. Mute

Gypsy Brazil, a colourful Latin-American nut; a fortune-teller

Hazel, an intelligent, though small, female nut; wears spectacles

William the Conker, a real tough, though pretty stupid, nut; lovable

Professor Jelly Bon-Bon (THE CHOCOLATE SQUIRTER), a confectioner of distinction in search of fine nuts for his fine chocolates; charmingly villainous

Old Ma Coconut, a raucous, large, strong female nut with a sharp tongue and a heart of gold

MUSICAL NUMBERS

ACT I

Come to the Nutty May Fair	Kernel Walnut, (Monkeynut) and Gypsy Brazil
A Little Bit of Learning	Hazel with Kernel Walnut, Gypsy Brazil and (Monkeynut)
William, Super-Nut	William the Conker, Kernel Walnut, Gypsy Brazil, (Monkeynut)
Nuts Needn't be Nuts	Hazel, Kernel Walnut, William the Conker, Gypsy Brazil and (Monkeynut)
Here I Come Gathering	Professor Jelly Bon-Bon
Nuts Needn't be Nuts (Reprise)	Hazel, Kernel Walnut, Gypsy Brazil and (Monkeynut)
The May Madrigal	Hazel
Old Ma Coconut	Kernel Walnut, Gypsy Brazil, Hazel and (Monkeynut)
Roll-a-Ball-a-Bowl-a-Ball	Old Ma Coconut with Kernel Walnut, Gypsy Brazil, Hazel and (Monkeynut)
The May Madrigal (Reprise) (Rehearsal)	Hazel, Kernel Walnut, Gypsy Brazil, Old Ma Coconut and (Monkeynut)
We're Gonna be Stars	Hazel, Kernel Walnut, Gypsy Brazil, Old Ma Coconut and (Monkeynut)
The May Madrigal (Reprise)	Hazel, Kernel Walnut, Gypsy Brazil and (Monkeynut) with Professor Jelly Bon-Bon

ACT II

Roll-a-Ball-a-Bowl-a-Ball (Reprise)	Old Ma Coconut
Carried Away	Hazel, Kernel Walnut and Gypsy Brazil
Here I Come Gathering (Reprise)	Professor Jelly Bon-Bon
Nuttiness is Best	Hazel, William the Conker, Kernel Walnut, Gypsy Brazil, Old Ma Coconut and (Monkeynut)
Chocolate Children	Professor Jelly Bon-Bon

Nuttiness is Best (Reprise) (Audience participation sequence)	William the Conker, Hazel, Kernel Walnut, Gypsy Brazil and (Monkeynut) with Audience
Come to the Nutty May Fair/Nuttiness is Best/The May Madrigal (Reprise)	The Company, except Professor Jelly Bon-Bon

The Vocal Score for this play is available from Samuel French Ltd.

PRODUCTION NOTES

The play takes place at the Nutty May Fair. The sideshows, booths, etc., should be imaginatively based on nut shapes, but colourful. If possible, **Old Ma Coconut**'s booth should be on a truck and only appear for her scenes. (See photographs of set.)

The other location, **Professor Jelly Bon-Bon**'s caravan, can be in front of the main set. Lighting can cut it off sufficiently from the fairground. It may be a good idea if the fairground booths revolve to become trees or bushes during the caravan scenes.

To increase the "Nutty Flavour", the shapes of the booths should echo nut shapes—for instance, **Gypsy Brazil**'s fortune-telling tent could look like a brazil nut standing on one end. **Monkeynut**'s cage should be visible, and **William the Conker**'s nutty boxing booth. And in its own area, **Old Ma Coconut**'s Shy. The Shy itself mustn't be revealed until the characters go to visit her, though a canvas awning advertizing her Shy could be visible, and this could later be raised or pulled aside to reveal her, sitting on her plinth-like pole.

Other booths could be visible, but are not used in the plot—e.g. "Mrs Acorn's Tea Stall", "Senor Pistachio's Ice Cream", "Gilbert the Filbert's Nutty-Go-Round", "Almondo's Nutty Dip—A Prize Every Time", or even, at the entrance, the "Cashew Desk". These should clearly not be over-done, or the audience will assume they are part of the story. However, it could well be possible to incorporate these characters into the show, or, rather into the experience in the theatre. For example, the Box Office could be transformed into the "Cashew Desk", with Box Office staff in costume. The Ice Cream in the interval could be sold from a stall by "Senor Pistachio" and his Assistant, and "Mrs Acorn" could serve tea. In other words, the play need not only be Acts I and II; the Fairground atmosphere can over-spill into the whole afternoon or evening.

If there were enough room in the Theatre, or outside it, "Gilbert The Filbert" could actually have a roundabout for the children to ride on. "Almondo's Nutty Dip" could be a real Bran Tub in the Foyer. All these ideas could not only involve Staff and others in the production, but be splendid publicity and incentives to buy ices, etc. To buy an ice cream from a Nut is more exciting than buying one from an Usherette.

It is important, however, not to anywhere suggest that any of the Fairground attractions involve eating nuts (e.g. "Nutburgers"), because this could pre-warn the audience of what might happen in the play. The Fairground is simply a Fair run by Nuts. It should be, discarding realism, colourful and bright, and the Nuts themselves, while retaining the shape of their name, should be dressed in human terms. Therefore **Kernel Walnut** is a walnut-shaped Ringmaster, **Gypsy Brazil** is a Brazil-Nut-Shaped Gypsy Fortune Teller, with Latin-American overtones.

ACT I

The Nutty May Fair

Before the formal beginning of the show, it is suggested that the tabs are already out, and the set in view. This consists of "Kernel Walnut's Nutty May Fair". All the fairground booths and sideshows could be suggested very simply with cut-out shapes

As the audience arrive and take their seats, it is suggested that Kernel Walnut mingles among them, welcoming them to his Fair, and, like a Fairground Barker, "calls" people to the Fairground, where shortly a Nutty Entertainment is to take place. Perhaps he bangs an Acorn Drum. Happy Fairground Organ Music plays. As the show starts, Kernel Walnut reaches the stage and the House Lights fade. Music. Dawn lighting. Kernel Walnut beckons on other Nuts as if they are arriving for the Fair. Maybe they bring on a booth with them.

SONG 1: **Come to the Nutty May Fair**

Kernel   Heigh-ho, come to the Nutty May Fair

The theme is picked up by other voices repeating the line and singing to "LA" in counterpoint. The section ends with a sung fanfare, as the Lighting increases and Kernel Walnut comes forward. The Other Nuts, who should be wearing cloaks to prevent their costumes being seen before their first major entrance, exit, or enter their booths

On stage is a trolley with an assortment of noise-making devices—a rattle, a horn, cymbals, drum, whistles etc. If the actor playing Kernel Walnut can manage it, it could be a complete one-man-band kit, complete with wash board, bass drum etc. In any event, during his opening announcement he uses the noises to punctuate the speech

(*noise*) Roll up. Roll up. (*noise*) Nutty novelties, nutty nonsenses, and novel nonsensical nuts. (*noise*) All the nutty fun of Kernel Walnut's Nutty May Fair.

If possible a Banner flies in with "KERNEL WALNUT'S NUTTY MAY FAIR" written on. Kernel Walnut could accompany himself on the one-man band, or simply with his various noises. After the first two lines of each chorus, the Other Nuts could pop their heads out to shout "Nutty, Nutty; Nutty, Nutty; Nutty Nutty Nut".

> (*singing*)
> Heigh-ho, come to the Nutty May Fair
> Heigh-ho, roll up for fun and fresh air
> We've stalls and we've sideshows
> Games you can play

So come and try your luck now
Just step up this way
Ev'ry Nut who is any Nut's bound to be there
So come to the Nutty May Fair
Come to the Nutty May Fair.

Other Nuts Surprises
Prizes
Lots to do and see
Kernel Thrills
Spills
All Ooohs and aaahs and wheeeeeeeee!

Kernel Heigh-ho, come to the Nutty May Fair
Heigh-ho, roll up for fun and fresh air ...

The music changes to a dramatic rumble

And first, Ladies and Gents all, Kernel Walnut proudly presents, for your awesome appreciation, that wild nutty beast, that savage beasty nut, captured with my own bare hands, fresh from the jungle, the one and only—Monkeynut!

He takes up a whip, cracks it, indicates Monkeynut's cage, and waits. Nothing happens

(*calling*) Monkeynut! (*He coughs. After a pause, to the audience*) As you were. (*Muttering as he goes to the cage in search*) Monkeynut, where the devil are you? (*Seeing the cage is empty*) Ahhhh! He's escaped! (*To the audience*) You haven't seen him by any chance? He's ferocious, uncivilized, ruthless ...

Monkeynut enters from the other side of the stage. He is cheeky and bouncy, nothing like the ferocious monster we have expected. He waves at the audience—he cannot speak

The audience shout out

Can you see him? You can? Where is he? Over there? Thank you.

Kernel Walnut runs over to where Monkeynut was, but by now he has crossed to his cage. He waves cheekily

He's not there at all! I think you were having me on! What? Over there? Thank you.

Kernel Walnut turns. Monkeynut has disappeared again—behind the cage

He's not there at all!

Monkeynut pops out again

He *is* there?

Kernel Walnut turns sharply and sees Monkeynut

There you are! Come here!

*Music as Kernel Walnut chases Monkeynut round the cage—once—twice.
The second time, Kernel Walnut pauses for breath. Monkeynut runs into him.
Kernel Walnut jumps, turns and starts chasing Monkeynut round the cage in
the other direction. On the second "round", Kernel Walnut opens the door of
the cage and Monkeynut runs into it. Kernel Walnut slams the door*

Got you, you cheeky creature! Stay in the cage.

*As the music starts, Monkeynut stretches the rubber bars of the cage and
creeps out of the cage*

SONG 1: **Come to the Nutty May Fair** (continued)

*Monkeynut joins in the routine by playing noises, taking Kernel Walnut by
surprise*

> Heigh-ho, come to the Nutty May Fair
> Heigh-ho, roll up for fun and fresh air
> Watch top entertainment
> Trials of skill
> We'll make you feel welcome
> If you've time to kill
> We've got Nuts that are common and Nuts that are rare ...

Dramatic rumble

And now, Ladies and Gents all, Kernel Walnut proudly presents that
astrological astronut extraordinary, gazing into the future through her
crystal nut, fortune-teller—Gypsy Brazil! (*He indicates her tent dramatically*)

Gypsy Brazil enters

SONG 1: **Come to the Nutty May Fair** (continued)

Gypsy   Aye, aye, aye, aye, aye, aye, aye,
> Aye, aye, aye, aye, aye, aye,
> I am Gypsy Brazil
> A Nut from Brazil—
> Where the Nuts come from—
> Aye, aye, aye, aye, aye
> Caramba

> Aye, aye, aye, aye, aye
> I like the samba
> And your future will be told
> If you cross my palm with gold—
> Or silver
> Or copper
> Or even amber!
> Aye, aye!

All three dance

Kernel } Heigh-ho, come to the Nutty May Fair
Gypsy } Heigh-ho, roll up for fun and fresh ...

Gypsy Aaaaah!

Gypsy Brazil stands dramatically gazing into her crystal nut. The other two freeze and stare too. The lighting could flash up and down to heighten the tension and, indeed, every time Gypsy Brazil has a twinge

A twinge. (*She shudders*) A twinge.
Kernel What fate does your twinge foretell? Foresee for us the immediate future.
Gypsy I see unrest, upheaval, the earth-a will quake ...
Kernel Where?
Gypsy Here.
Kernel (*alarmed*) Here?
Gypsy (*pointing, without looking*) There!
Kernel There?
Gypsy Under our very nose.
Kernel No!
Gypsy (*nodding*) Nose.

Kernel Walnut closes his eyes, nervous. Gypsy Brazil continues to look in the crystal nut. Tension music. The earth near them, or beneath them, begins to quake. A whole mound, of part of an earth bank, moves, if possible causing earth to be thrown up. They gasp and turn away in fright. Then they look again. More earth moves or jumps in the air. They gasp and turn away, then gingerly turn back. From underground is emerging someone digging his or her way up. They all step back nervously

Another Nut, Hazel, steps from the earth. She confidently brushes off the surplus earth

The other Nuts stare at her, open-mouthed. Hazel puts on her spectacles and notices them

Hazel (*matter of fact*) Good morning.
Kernel (*bemused*) Good morning.
Gypsy Hi.
Hazel What are you doing here?
Kernel We——er—actually I was about to ask you the same question.
Hazel (*confidently*) You weren't here yesterday. I particularly spotted that this place was unpopulated.
Kernel Pardon?
Hazel Granted.
Kernel We arrived at dawn. Kernel Walnut—(*he bows*)—and his Nutty May Fair.
Hazel How do you do, *Juglans regia*.

They shake hands

Kernel Eh? Oh. How do you do? (*introducing*) This is Gypsy Brazil.
Hazel *Bertholletia excelsa!* Hello.
Gypsy Hi.
Kernel And this is my pet wild nut, Monkeynut.

Monkeynut waves and does a silly movement

Hazel *Arachis hypogaea!* Hello.

Monkeynut reacts

Kernel Why are you calling us names?
Gypsy It's rude to call nuts names.
Hazel Sorry, but they're your proper names.
Gypsy (*heated*) You mean there is something *im*proper about "Gypsy Brazil"?
Hazel No, no. But *Bertholletia excelsa* is the original Latin name. Mine's *Corylus avellana*, but other nuts call me Hazel. Now, if you'll excuse me, I'd better be off, or I'll miss algebra.
Kernel Where are you meeting her?
Hazel I beg your pardon?
Kernel This er—Algy nut.
Hazel No, no. I'll miss the algebra *lesson*. Algebra is a branch of mathematics, like arithmetic or geometry or trigonometry.

Blank faces stare back

I'm sorry, I'd better explain. I live on a tree—a hazel—that happens to grow in a school playground, overlooking a classroom, so if a window is open I can hear the lessons, see the blackboard and learn things. It's called education.
Gypsy Education?
Hazel Yes. (*Elated*) I'm an educated nut!

SONG 2: **A Little Bit of Learning**

> A little bit of learning
> Goes a long, long way
> You would enjoy it.
> A little bit of learning
> Helps you on your way
> If you employ it.
>
> Arithmetic or Geography
> Hist'ry, French or Writing
> Lit'rature or Geometry
> Can really be exciting.
>
> 'Cos
> A little bit of learning
> Goes a long, long way
> You pick up knowledge.

> A little bit of learning
> Helps you on your way
> From school or college.
>
> With Reading, Art, Biology
> Physics, Maths or Spanish
> German, Gym or Chemistry
> Your ignorance will vanish.

All (*becoming enthusiastic*)
      Yes
      A little bit of learning
      Goes a long, long way
Hazel   So don't decry it.
All   A little bit of learning
      Starting from today
Hazel   You ought to try it.

All   A little bit of learning
      Goes a long, long way
Hazel   Don't underrate it.
All   A little bit of learning
Hazel   Means that I can say—
      I'm educated!

At the end of the song the others applaud

Kernel What a marvellous opportunity. I'd give my wrinkles for it. To learn. To know.

Gypsy What *I* want to know is what an, how you say, educated nut is-a doing under the ground.

Kernel On an expedition, eh? Exploring? I remember in the Royal Nut Regiment ...

Hazel (*laughing*) No, no. Some stupid squirrel decided to kidnap me and bury me. Part of his hoard, I suppose.

Gypsy (*shocked*) A squirrel? Didn't he bite you?

Hazel No, I didn't struggle. Seemed the most sensible thing to do. I let him bury me, waited a while, then started digging my way out.

Kernel What a brilliant campaign! What strategy!

Gypsy Bravo! Bravo!

Kernel Listen, Hazel, old thing. Stick around for a bit and see the Fair, eh? All that learning—well, you need a break.

Gypsy I'll tell-a your fortune.

Kernel You can see all the sideshows.

Hazel Well, to be honest, it all sounds a bit time-wasting.

Monkeynut goes to the drum

Kernel Stuff and nonsense. Enjoy yourself.

Monkeynut bangs the drum urgently

It's time for a sideshow now! Sit and watch. Eh?

Hazel (*after a pause*) Very well. Thank you.
Gypsy Bravo!

Gypsy sits her down in a good spot to see the next "Act". Kernel returns to address the audience, accompanied by drum rolls from Monkeynut

Kernel And now, Ladies and Gents all. The toughest nut in the world, strong-nut, super-nut, the one and only—William the Conker!

From the Boxing Booth, William the Conker enters, in shorts and wearing boxing gloves. His arms are raised as he acknowledges the applause. Then he spoils the effect by falling down the step. He gets up

SONG 3: **William, Super-Nut**

William	William Super-Nut I am the Greatest
Kernel **Gypsy** }	He is the Greatest William Super-Nut
William	I am the Champion
Kernel **Gypsy** } **All**	He is the Champion William the Conker Ra, ra, ra.

The music continues as William goes into his Act, assisted by Monkeynut. First, Monkeynut hands him a "solid" steel bar. After all the preliminary concentration palaver, William, accompanied by a drum roll, bends the steel bar almost double. He looks up for applause. He acknowledges it by letting go of one end of the bar in order to raise his arm. It springs back and hits him under the chin, sending him reeling backwards. Next, Kernel and Monkeynut struggle on with a large weight, say "one ton", with a ring as a handle. Alternatively, it is on the end of a rope, and Kernel "flies" it in. Dramatic rumble as William prepares for his Act of Strength, rippling his muscles, etc. He stands behind the weight and concentrates really hard—closing his eyes. He slowly lowers himself until he can take the ring handle in his mouth; then, eyes still closed, he quivers with effort as he starts to lift. Without him apparently noticing, the handle comes off in his teeth. He straightens up, and walks a few paces, face racked with strain, leaving the weight behind. Then he returns and lowers the handle back to the weight, before opening his eyes and triumphantly taking his applause. The weight is removed

SONG 3: **William, Super-Nut** (continued)

William	William Super-Nut I am the Greatest

Kernel	
Kernel	He is the Greatest
Gypsy	

Kernel And now, Ladies and Gents all, the most extraordinary nutty boxing contest ever between, in the blue corner—

William goes there. The ring is mimed

Kernel	William
Gypsy	Super-Nut

William I am the Champion

Kernel	
Gypsy	He is the Champion

Kernel (*speaking*) And in the red corner—

William goes there

Kernel	William the Conker
Gypsy	Ra, ra, ra.

Gypsy Brazil rings a bell on the trolley. Monkeynut acts as referee

Kernel (*commentating*) Round one, and straightaway William's on the attack, with short sharp jabs to his body. He's looking fit, full of bounce, just eyeing himself up, not wanting to do too much too soon. Ooh! Well, he took himself by surprise there, a good, strong body punch, but he retaliates with a right to the head, and a left and a right. He's stunned himself. No, no, he's all right, the referee just breaking him from a clinch. Breathing heavily now as he warily shadows himself, waiting for an opening. And there it is.

William goes mad

Left, right, left, right, arms flailing, his body locked in itself. Oh, and a good uppercut. Ouch. And another. He's weakening. A blow to the body. And another. He's making mincemeat of himself. Oh, and he walked right into that one. And he's down. He's down.

Monkeynut "counts him out"

One, Two, Three, Four, Five, struggling to get up, Seven, he's not going to make it, Nine, TEN. He's knocked himself out!

Applause. Monkeynut fans William with a towel. During the fight, Gypsy offers vocal encouragement: "Aye, aye, aye"—"yip, yip, yip"—"caramba", and other Latin-American expressions of excitement

Gypsy Bravo! Bravo! (*to Hazel*) It was a close fight, yes?
Hazel Well, to be honest, I thought it was rather silly.
Gypsy Silly?
Hazel Well, it's obvious. A boxing match requires two boxers. William boxes with himself. That's silly.

Gypsy No. Is not silly. By always boxing with himself, William has won every contest in his career.

Hazel Yes, but he's also *lost* every contest in his career. Look at him. He's still out for the count. It's stupid.

Kernel But Hazel, old thing, you're forgetting, William the Conker is a nut ...

Gypsy We're *all* nuts ...

Gypsy does an odd movement which should, for the first time, instil into the audience the idea of the "Nuts" (characters) and the "nuts" (stupid) pun

Kernel And this is the *Nutty* May Fair. We're proud of that.

Hazel But I'm proud of being a nut, too.

Kernel Ah yes, but you're a special nut.

Gypsy Like you say. An educated nut.

Hazel But don't you see? (*Indicating William*) A display like that by a nut like that gives nuts everywhere a bad name.

Gypsy But you say earlier we have "good" names—(*proudly*) *Bertholletia excelsa* ...

Hazel I didn't mean that. Look ...

SONG 4: **Nuts Needn't be Nuts**

During this song, William revives, takes in what is happening and happily joins in the choruses. During the first chorus Hazel could stand on an improvised soap box

Hazel   Nuts need not be nuts
        Why should Nuts be nutty?
        Nuts unite
        Let's protest
        Show the world
        We're not second best
        Raise our status
        Make the world appreciate us
        No ifs, no buts
        Nuts needn't be nuts.

   (*speaking*) Well, will you join me?

Kernel, Gypsy and Monkeynut shuffle uncomfortably, uncertain of how to react

        Don't be so dense
        You know that it makes sense
        There's all the evidence
        To go on—
        Bats aren't all batty
        Pots aren't all potty
        Screws aren't all screwy
        Dots aren't all dotty
        Loops aren't all loopy—
        And so on—

> Nuts need not be nuts
> Why should Nuts be nutty
> Nuts unite
> Let's protest
> Show the world
> We're not second best
> Raise our status
> Make the world appreciate us
> No ifs, no buts
> Nuts needn't be nuts.

Kernel Oh, I don't know. What should we do? (*To the audience*) What do *you* think we should do? Should we join Hazel?

He encourages the audience to answer. Whatever they shout, suddenly Gypsy Brazil has a twinge

Gypsy Aaaaaaah!

> Aye, aye, aye, aye, aye
> Caramba
> I have a twinge that say
> Hazel is right
> Nuts unite
> Fight for respect from today.

All cheer and with fervour join in the song

All   Nuts need not be nuts
> Why should Nuts be nutty
> Nuts unite
> Let's protest
> Show the world
> We're not second best
> Raise our status

Kernel⎫
Gypsy⎬ Hazel stay and educate us
William⎭

Hazel   No ifs, no buts
> Nuts needn't be nuts.

All   Nuts need not be nuts
> Why should Nuts be nutty?
> Nuts unite
> Let's protest
> Show the world
> We're not second best
> Raise our status
> Make the world appreciate us

   Make the world emancipate us
   No ifs, no buts
   Nuts needn't be nuts.

At the end of the song All are radiant

Hazel We'll show the world—nuts by name, not nuts by nature.
William Hear, hear.
Kernel We may be thick-skinned, but in a nutshell there's more than meets the eye!
William Hear, hear.
Gypsy Oh, caramba, I'm-a so elated I could cry. (*She sobs*)
William Hear, hear. I mean—there, there. (*He puts his arm around her*)
Kernel Now, strategy. Hazel, what's our plan of campaign?
Hazel Well, first I have to make sure you all think the same way as I do.
Kernel Quite. You must have a united front behind you.
William How can you have a front behind you?

Gypsy Brazil laughs

Hazel (*looking at William*) We must make sure that all of us have the intelligence to cope with liberation.
William I mean, you can't have a behind in front of you so how can you have a front behind you? A front's in front. A behind's behind. A side is on the side. Well, that's different 'cos there might be more than one side. There's this side and that side and upside and downside ...

He becomes aware of everyone looking at him. Embarrassed pause

Hazel I'm sorry, Kernel, but you must see, William is just too nutty to be one of us.
Kernel (*after a pause of realization*) You mean—you think he should leave the Fair?

Hazel nods

  But, I say, that's a bit strong, isn't it?
William (*not realizing the danger he's in*) I'm right, aren't I? 'Cos if I'm standing here I can see in *front*, but I can't see behind. Well, not unless I jump round—(*he demonstrates*)—but then I can't see in *front*; well, I *can* see in front, but it's a different front 'cos it's what was behind *before* I jumped ...

Hazel looks firmly at Kernel, who realizes he must get rid of William. He taps him on the shoulder. William turns

Kernel William, old chap ...
Gypsy Oh, Kernel, must we?

Kernel shrugs, as if to say "we must"

Kernel William—I'm sorry, but—I'm afraid it's good-bye. (*He shakes hands*)

William Good-bye, Kernel. Where are you going?
Kernel No. (*Gently*) You're going, old chap.
William Me?

Kernel Walnut nods

Aren't I going to be liberated?

Kernel shakes his head

I want to be liberated.

Kernel shakes his head

I'll go and pack my nutcase, then. (*He moves to the Boxing Booth*)

Monkeynut, who has been watching, comes running forward to remonstrate. He pulls at Kernel and Gypsy

Kernel Sorry, Monkeynut. I know he was your friend, but it had to happen.
Gypsy (*regretfully*) With him around no-one would take us seriously.
Hazel To be honest, the same applies to Monkeynut ...
Kernel Oh no, Hazel, please. I'm all for your new strategy, but I have to draw the line. Monkeynut is my pet. I've had him since he sprouted.
Hazel All right. (*She looks meaningfully at Monkeynut*) But he'll have to work really hard to improve himself.
Kernel He will, he will.
Hazel Now, to business.
Gypsy (*excited again*) Aye, aye, aye, aye, aye. (*She sings*) Nuts need not be nuts, cha, cha, cha!
Kernel Forward to my nuttyvan ...

Music

   Gypsy, Kernel and Hazel exit excitedly

The music changes to a sad version of "William, Super-Nut". William emerges from the Boxing Booth. He carries his nut-case. He and Monkeynut mime their sad good-byes. A handshake, then an impulsive hug

   William exits, with a final wave; he goes off the opposite side to the one used by Hazel and the others

Monkeynut stands, torn between loyalty to Kernel and friendship for William. He starts off in one direction, then stops, changes his mind, and starts off in the other direction. Finally he resolves to follow his friend William. He dashes off in that direction, then stops, has a final nostalgic look at the Nutty May Fair, and waves it good-bye

   Monkeynut exits in pursuit of William

The lighting changes to another area—possibly downstage. This can be "elsewhere"—i.e. NOT at the Fair, another location: but it need not be a specified place

   Music as Professor Jelly Bon-Bon enters with his caravan, on wheels. He

*advertises his wares, talking to the audience as potential customers. He is
dressed something like a high-class chef. On his caravan is written "Jelly
Bon-Bon"*

Jelly Sweeties, candies, choccychocs! Sweeties, candies, choccychocs! (*He
sees the audience*) Aha! Customers. Ladies, gentlemen, young ladies,
young gentlemen, you have had the fair fortune to bump into—
(*bowing*)—Professor Jelly Bon-Bon, at your service. Presenting Professor
Jelly Bon-Bon's exclusive range of sweeties, candies and choccychocs,
fashioned by my own fair hands in all your favourite flavours. Mango
fruit drop fondants, creme de menthe turkish delight, marzipan truffles,
peppermint wafers. (*He comes to the edge of the stage, showing samples of
his sweets, on a tray or in a basket*) Stop me and try one, you don't have to
buy one, a sample is perfectly free, Taste one and I'm sure, you'll long for
some more—just take one and suck it and see!
Box upon box of chocs in stock—for sale at competitive prices.
If your tooth is sweet
Give it a treat
With ...

*Suddenly a total surprise—he stops, drops his charming smile and listens, then
sniffs. Music, as he picks up a scent, and follows it a few paces. He has a look
of grim determination on his face, totally different from the suave salesman.
The scent seems to vanish*

(*Frustrated*) Aaagh. Nothing. Damnation. (*Realizing he has got carried
away in front of customers*) Sweeties, candies, choccychocs! (*but it lacks
conviction*) Sweeties, candies, oh—(*noise of frustration*)—oh ...! Forgive
me, friends, forgive me. I thought ...! But I mustn't tell *you*. Oh, why not?
I'll cast caution to the wind and spill the choccy beans. You see, this
caravan, this sales spiel is but a cover for my main purpose here. True, I
furnish the famous with fine confectionery, but—and it's a big but—
BUT, my *most* fine, my *super*-fine chocs, the kind I am most expert at
making, the kind my best customers best like—(*he looks around. Confi-
dentially*)—they can only be made really fresh at this time of year—(*he
sniffs, hoping to find a scent*)—because only at this time of the year—(*he
whispers*)—in a place such as this, can I discover the correct—ingredients.
(*He sniffs again*)

SONG 5: **Here I Come Gathering**

Jelly   Oh
Here I come gathering nuts in May
Nuts in May
Nuts in May
Here I come gathering nuts in May
On a bright and breezy afternoon.

Yes
Here I come gathering nuts in May
Nuts in May

Nuts in May
Here I come gathering nuts in May
Nutty nuts to make my choccychocs.

I'll catch them and squirt them with chocolate
Then wrap them and box them to sell
A special selection
Of high class confection'ry
Guaranteed quality, bound to sell well.

He sniffs again. This time he gets a nutty scent and reacts excitedly through the final chorus

So
Here I come gathering nuts in May
Nuts in May
Nuts in May
Here I come gathering nuts in May
Nutty nuts to make my fortune with.

He takes from his caravan a huge pair of nutcrackers. He hides with them, out of sight. The music changes to a dramatic rumble

William enters carrying his nut-case, on his way from the Fair. Fed up, he looks at the ground

The audience will probably shout a warning to him, especially when Professor Jelly creeps from behind his caravan, ending up stalking William and finally grabbing him from behind, inside the nutcrackers

(*In triumph*) Gotcha!

William drops his nut-case in surprise. Professor Jelly swings him round to look at him. Meanwhile, William takes in what has happened

William 'Ere! What's going on?

William flexes his muscular arms, and takes the "blades" of the nutcrackers, which hug his waist, and with all his strength, struggles to force them open. Both William and Professor Jelly puff and grunt and strain, but William is too strong for Professor Jelly, who realizes he has taken on too much. Finally William escapes, the nutcrackers end up on the ground, and Professor Jelly rubs his arms

Now. What's your game, mister?
Jelly (*angrily*) Game? This isn't a—(*having an idea*)—a game? Of course, that's exactly what it is—a game. Ha ha ha.

William does not laugh

A jolly jape. A joke. Ha ha ha.
William I know a joke.
Jelly Eh?

William I know a joke.

Jelly Really?

William Yeah. What do you need to post a pair of shoes?

Jelly What do I need to post a pair of shoes? I don't know.

William A stamp on them. (*He stamps hard on Professor Jelly's feet, and roars with laughter*)

Jelly Aaaaaaah! (*hopping with pain*) Ho, ho, ho, very comical, very droll. Who are you?

William (*in a flat voice*) Strong-nut, super-nut, the one and only William the Conker. Toughest nut in the world.

Jelly (*rubbing his foot*) You can say that again.

William Right. Strong-nut, super-nut, the one and only ...

Jelly (*sharply*) No, no, no ...

William (*threateningly*) What?

Jelly No, no—no wonder I couldn't catch you ... I mean, not that I was *really* trying to catch you—(*aside, to the audience*)—and, anyway, conkers make rotten chocolates ... (*to William*) Where are you going?

William I don't know.

Jelly Why not?

William I haven't got there yet.

Jelly I see. Where have you come from?

William The Fair.

Jelly The Fair? Which fair?

William The Nutty May Fair.

Jelly (*excitedly*) Nutty? Did you say nutty?

William Yeah. Some new nut comes, says I'm nuts and the other nuts give me the push, see?

Jelly I think so.

William Rotten lot of nuts they were. Rotten.

Jelly (*worried*) You mean—diseased? (*More worried*) Or deceased?

William They treated me rotten.

Jelly I see. (*He has an idea*) Do you fancy getting your own back on them?

William No. There's nothing I can do.

Jelly Work for me, William, work for me. Professor Jelly Bon-Bon at your service. I am gathering nuts for my exclusive range of chocolates. Assist me and no nut will dare—er—treat you rotten again.

William Yeah, well—(*to the audience*)—the other nuts asked for it, didn't they? So I'll let 'em have it. Yeah? All right.

He shakes hands with Professor Jelly, who cringes with the strength of the squeeze

Jelly Splendid. I'll give you a scrub and you can start immediately.

William A scrub?

Jelly A scrub. You're grubby. A grubby nut may be a germy nut and a germy nut could infect a confection and affect my sales. Not to mention my reputation.

William Your reputation?

Jelly I said not to mention my reputation.

Suddenly Professor Jelly changes tack again by going into his sniffing routine.
He follows a scent towards the side William entered from

William Are you all right?
Jelly Shhhh. I can smell a nut.
William Maybe it's me. Ha ha.
Jelly Shhh. It's coming. William the Conker, this is your chance to shine.
  (*He hands him the nutcrackers*) Catch it. But don't crack it. I want my nuts
  whole, no bruises. Meanwhile, I'll get ready to receive it. (*He excitedly
  goes inside his caravan*)

Music as William prepares for action. He experiments with the nutcrackers to
see how they work, then lumbers round behind the caravan to wait. Pause

  Monkeynut enters in search of William, his friend

He sees the caravan, and, intrigued, goes to look at it. He walks the length of
it, then carries on round the back, just as William emerges round the front the
other end. William looks bemused—there is no sign of a Nut. He walks the
length of the caravan and, just as Monkeynut did, carries on round the back

The audience may be shouting out warnings, though in fact their loyalties
could well be divided. They "like" both characters, but one of them has become
a "Baddie"—for very good reasons, which makes it more difficult to see the
situation in black and white terms

Monkeynut re-emerges, having gone all the way round, and stops to look at the
writing on the side of the caravan. William re-emerges the same end, having
completed the circle too. Unaware of Monkeynut's presence, he looks off in the
other direction, i.e. the direction Monkeynut came from. Both Nuts are now in
such a position that they can both take a few steps backwards, Monkeynut in
order to see the writing more clearly, William to get a better view. Panto-style,
they bump into each other back to back. Both react by jumping violently.
Monkeynut, quaking, is rooted to the spot and does not turn round. William
turns, sees a Nut, and swiftly brings the nutcrackers over Monkeynut's head
and catches him. Monkeynut struggles. William swings him round to face the
audience, and then back again. Suddenly the music stops and the action seems
to freeze

William (*realizing, to himself, but taking in the audience*) It's my friend,
  Monkeynut. Isn't it?
Audience Yes.

William thinks for a moment, then lets the nutcrackers drop round Monkey-
nut's ankles. Then, without Monkeynut ever having seen William face to face,
William pushes him off, back the way he came

  Monkeynut scurries off, too terrified to turn back

William looks after Monkeynut, then takes in the caravan, realizing that there
will be trouble from Jelly as he has not caught the nut. He has an idea.
Suddenly, complete with grunts and groans, he goes into his "Boxing with
Himself" routine. After a few blows, falls and self-clinches, and a fair amount
of noise, Professor Jelly emerges from the caravan to see what is going on

Jelly What's happening? William!

William turns to see Professor Jelly. He has just thrown a punch, so his arm is extended. Professor Jelly has to duck to avoid the arm. But William continues spinning round, and as Professor Jelly stands upright again, he gets William's gloved fist straight in his head. This sends him reeling, furious

William!

William is still fighting with himself

William!

William stops sheepishly

(*wildly*) Where's the nut? Where's the nut?

William What nut?

Jelly What do you mean, "What nut?" The nut I ordered you to catch.

William It got away.

Jelly What?

William Too strong for me.

Jelly Rubbish. Toughest nut in the world you said you were.

William Yeah, but he was all wriggly and wiry and I couldn't hold him. You know what monkeynuts are.

Jelly Monkeynut? Was it a monkeynut?

William Yeah.

Jelly (*calming down*) Oh. Well, in that case—monkeynuts—most inferior variety, most unsuitable. You're forgiven, William. But next time, you will perform better.

Music, as Professor Jelly utters the first direct threat to "our" nuts

You will catch me the *best* nuts—a walnut for a tasty walnut whirl, a brazil for a juicy brazil crunch and a hazel to finish off a delicious hazel cluster. Come, William. To the Nutty May Fair!

Professor Jelly and William exit, pulling the caravan

The lighting changes to bring us back to the Fairground. It is night

Kernel, Gypsy and Hazel, enter carrying lanterns. Hazel also carries a banner—"NUTS NEED NOT BE NUTS"

SONG 5: **Nuts Needn't be Nuts** (Reprise)

Hazel ⎫	Nuts need not be nuts
Kernel ⎪	Why should Nuts be nutty?
Gypsy ⎬	Nuts unite
Monkeynut ⎭	Let's protest
	Show the world
	We're not second best
	Raise our status
	Make the world appreciate us
	Make the world not underrate us
	No ifs, no buts
	Nuts needn't be nuts.

Hazel Now then, all that remains is to decide *how* we can improve the image of nuts, impressing the world with our skill.

Kernel Good show.

Gypsy Aye, aye, aye. Quite right.

Hazel Good idea.

Gypsy What?

Hazel Write!

Gypsy Write?

Hazel Right! Can you write a book? Or a poem?

Gypsy I cannot even write-a my name.

Hazel Mmm. What about art? Kernel, do you paint?

Kernel Oh, indeed I do. I enjoy painting.

Hazel What sort of things do you paint? Landscapes? Still life?

Kernel Well, mostly signs—like that one. (*He points to a fairground sign*)

Hazel I see.

Pause. All look a little gloomy

Got it!

Gypsy Got what?

Hazel A madrigal.

Kernel Does it hurt?

Hazel No! We'll do a madrigal.

Gypsy Aye, aye, of course! I adore to dance. (*She immediately starts doing an energetic, unbridled exhibition, accompanied by sounds, claps, etc.*) Brrrr. Caramba! Yip, yip, yip! (*She stops*)

Hazel What was that?

Gypsy A mad wriggle.

Hazel No.

Gypsy (*affronted*) That is what you said.

Hazel No. I said "madrigal". It's a type of song, quite difficult to sing, and it celebrates the merry month of May and the arrival of summer.

Kernel Sounds somewhat straight-faced and straight-laced to me.

Hazel No, it's not. It's fun. The children at the school learnt it. They sang it at a concert and everyone clapped and cheered and said how clever they were. (*She writes on the back of her banner*)

Gypsy Teach it to us, Hazel. And everyone will-a say how clever we are too.

Kernel All right, you've won me over. When's zero hour?

Hazel Tonight. (*She turns round her "poster" which reads "TONIGHT: MAY MADRIGAL: HERE"*)

Here's the poster to advertise it.

Kernel Tonight?

Gypsy Caramba! We will never be ready. (*She gets in a flap*)

Hazel Yes, we will. We'll start practising now. Listen, it goes like this.

SONG 6: **The May Madrigal**

Hazel   It's the merry, merry month of May
                   Fa la la la la la fol de rol de ray
                   And the summer is on its way ...

She stops, because she notices Gypsy stiffen

Gypsy Aaaaaaaah!
Hazel (*speaking*) What is it?
Kernel She's having one of her twinges. (*He holds Gypsy to support her*) Where's her crystal nut? (*He finds it in her pocket, and places it before her eyes*)
Gypsy Aaaaaaaaaah!
Kernel It's a bad one. (*assuming a strange voice*) What do you see, Gypsy Brazil, what do you see?

Music

Gypsy I see danger. Now.
Kernel For us?
Gypsy (*after a pause*) No. For another nut. Running, Running. Scared. Frightened. Running. Here.

She turns to look off. The others follow her gaze

Running here. See!

Monkeynut enters from the other side

The trio are looking off in the wrong direction. Monkeynut approaches and taps all three on the shoulder, making them jump and turn. They see him

Ahh! Monkeynut!
Kernel Don't do that. Creeping up on us. It's not funny.

Monkeynut trembles, his whole body shuddering

Hazel I don't think he's trying to be funny. He's in quite a state.
Kernel Apologies, Monkeynut. Didn't mean to bark. Come on, old thing, what is it?

Monkeynut starts to mime his unpleasant experience. Kernel interprets. Monkeynut flings his arms round Kernel's waist

All right. Good boy. I know you love me. I love you too. But tell me what happ ...

Monkeynut shakes his head, and repeats the mime in the air

No? Oh. Someone hugged you?

Monkeynut looks ferocious, and does the mime with more strength

Someone *caught* you?

*Monkeynut nods and shakes his head—i.e. he is trying to say he was caught by some*thing *rather than some*one. *He mimes something round his waist, and trying to escape from it*

You were caught in a trap?

Monkeynut nods

And tried to escape?

Monkeynut nods

Something gripped you?

Monkeynut nods

(*To the audience*) What gripped him?

Audience Nutcrackers.

Kernel I beg your pardon?

Audience Nutcrackers.

Kernel (*terror in his eyes*) Not—not—nutcrackers?

Monkeynut nods and flings himself into Kernel's arms. Dramatic chord

Gypsy (*very frightened*) No, no. Not nutcrackers. Please. (*She falls sobbing into Kernel's arms too*)

Hazel Nutcrackers? What are they?

Kernel (*the voice of doom*) Oh, Hazel. All that education, yet you remain ignorant of basic nut-lore. Every year at this time, many innocent, life-loving nuts vanish mysteriously. With no warning they disappear and are never seen again.

Hazel But why?

Kernel Legend has it that a man catches them with a strong device—nut-crackers—and then, and this is the worst part, covers them … with chocolate.

Hazel Who is he?

Kernel We call him—the Chocolate Squirter.

Dramatic chord. Gypsy sobs still more violently at the mention of the name. Pause

Hazel Oh, come on. You don't believe that superstitious twaddle, do you?

Gypsy (*firmly*) Is not twaddle. Is true.

Hazel But think of all we talked about. You're liberated nuts now. Intelligent. And your common sense should tell you there is no such thing as this Chocolate Squirter—

Gypsy (*scared*) You shouldn't-a talk like this.

Hazel —and even if there *is*, you have nothing to fear from such a monster, because you are now clever enough to deal with him.

Kernel Oh Hazel, it's not as simple as that.

Hazel It is.

Kernel For you, maybe. But we can't change in the twinkling of an eye. All the fear of our ancestors in the nut-lore they passed down to us is firmly embedded under our shells. Give us time. Give us time.

Hazel But time to learn the May madrigal is running out. And we've advertised it; we'll look very silly if we have to cancel.

Kernel (*giving in, deflated, with very little enthusiasm*) All right. Teach us it now.

Gypsy No. No. Is not safe here. (*Stiffening*) I feel it, I feel it. Danger.

Monkeynut starts pointing in the direction of the Coconut Shy, trying to get Kernel's attention

Kernel What is it? Go somewhere else? Where?

Monkeynut mimes throwing balls at a coconut shy

Of course, excellent wheeze. The Coconut Shy.
Hazel What?
Kernel We can practise the madrigal there.
Gypsy Bravo! (*Explaining*) Old Ma Coconut is the largest nut in the Fair. We will be safe with her.

SONG 7: **Old Ma Coconut**

Gypsy	Perched up high
	In the Coconut Shy
	Watchful and weatherbeaten
	Giving fun
	Still un-won
	Determined never to be eaten
Kernel	She's our best bet
	Wouldn't you say?

Gypsy nods

All	We had best get
	Going right away.

During the song, carrying their lanterns, they move to the Coconut Shy. Monkeynut takes his drum and hooter. This "journey" might best be taken through the auditorium. This could help the scene change

> Old Ma Coconut will protect us
> Old Ma Coconut will know what to do
> She's the biggest Nut in the fair by far
> Nuts in danger all run to Ma
> She's the guiding star
> In the nutty sky
> Yes, Old Ma Coconut will protect us, so
> Let's go to the Coconut Shy.
>
> Old Ma Coconut is the answer
> Old Ma Coconut's is the place to hide
> If we stay with her then we won't get hurt
> Choc'late Squirter won't dare to squirt
> She will not desert
> Us when she knows why
> Yes, Old Ma Coconut is the answer, so
> Let's go to the Coconut Shy.

She may live in a Coconut Shy
But a shy coconut
She's not
Deep down she's the milk of nutty kindness
But a shell rough and tough
She's got.

Yes, Old Ma Coconut will protect us
Old Ma Coconut will know what to do
She's the biggest Nut in the fair by far
Nuts in danger all run to Ma
She's the guiding star
In the nutty sky
Yes, Old Ma Coconut will protect us, so
Let's go to the Coconut
Fly to the Coconut
Hie to the Coconut Shy.

They arrive at the Coconut Shy

Old Ma Coconut is discovered perched on her pole, fast asleep, snoring heavily. A few balls lie on the ground. Gypsy is in such a position that she has not yet seen Old Ma Coconut

Kernel She's dropped off.
Gypsy (*screaming*) Aaaaaah!
Kernel Shhh. What is it?
Gypsy (*sobbing*) Is her shell broken?
Kernel No, no. Not dropped off—(*he mimes falling from a height*)—dropped off. (*He snores, with eyes closed*)
Gypsy Oh, caramba, thank goodness.
Hazel Shall we wake her up?

Hazel goes to shake the pole. The others hold up their hands in horror

Kernel Hazel! No! Old Ma Coconut won't help unless we wake her up in the correct and considerate coconut manner. Now, forward everybody, very, very quietly.

All put down their lanterns. Hazel follows the example of the others. Each picks up a ball from beneath the pole, then backs gingerly away again, shushing each other. Then they kneel at firing range. All look at Kernel

(*Whispering*) Stand by.

In military fashion all draw their arms back ready to fire

(*Shouting loudly*) FIRE!

All noisily and enthusiastically fire balls at Old Ma Coconut: this is the correct way to wake a coconut. Suddenly she wakes up and looks down at the others, automatically going into her fairground barking routine

SONG 8: **Roll-a-Ball-a-Bowl-a-Ball**

Old Ma	Roll-a-Ball-a-Bowl-a-Ball
	Roll-a-Ball-a-Bowl
	Roll-a-Ball-a-Bowl-a-Ball
	Knock me off me pole.

Year after year
I've sat up 'ere
Letting the public attack me
But no-one's ever knocked me off
No-one can even crack me.

Ball after ball
Without one fall
May lead the public to hate me
But no-one's gonna take me home
Or try to dessicate me.

All	Roll-a-Ball-a-Bowl-a-Ball
Old Ma	Roll-a-Ball-a-Bowl
All	Roll-a-Ball-a-Bowl-a-Ball
Old Ma	Knock me off me pole.

'Nough is enough
I may be tough
But I can't hang around gaily chatting
I might be taken off my guard
And end up coconut matting.

All	Roll-a-Ball-a-Bowl-a-Ball
	Roll-a-Ball-a-Bowl
	Roll-a-Ball-a-Bowl-a-Ball
Old Ma	Knock me off me pole.

(*Speaking*) What do you lot want?

Kernel Sorry to intrude, Old Ma Coconut. Emergency. We fear the annual visitation by the Chocolate Squirter.

Old Ma What? If that little squirt tries to squirt one of us I'll squirt *him* so hard he won't never squirt no-one again no more never.

Gypsy Bravo. I feel safer already.

Old Ma Who's that? I ain't never noticed that nut before.

Kernel This is Hazel.

Hazel How do you do, *Cocos nucifera*.

Old Ma Wotcha.

Gypsy Hazel is very kindly teaching us a May madrigal, Ma.

Old Ma A what?

Hazel It's a kind of song, Old Ma Coconut. Would you care to join in?

Kernel It's to raise our status.

Old Ma Eh?

Kernel Our status. To raise it. Higher.

Old Ma I'm raised as high as I wanna be, darlin. The higher you get, the windier it gets, that's my motto. But I'll have a bash at the number.
Hazel Good.

Old Ma Coconut clears her throat very loudly. The others react.

Now this is how it goes.

SONG 8a: **The May Madrigal** (reprise)

> It's the merry, merry month of May
> Fa la la la la la fol de rol de ray
> And the summer is on its way
> Fa la la la la la fol de rol de ray
> Now spring is done
> Here comes the sun
> Fa la la la la la fol de rol de ray
> It's the merry, merry month of May
> Fa la la la la la fol de rol de ray.

All applaud

Old Ma Oh yeah, very upmarket that. I didn't understand all the words. Foreign were they? All that fol de diddle fa.
Hazel No, they're traditional, passed down through the ages. Now, those are the lines you sing. So all together. After three. (*She sings to demonstrate*)

> Fa la la la la la fol de rol de ray.

(*standing ready to conduct*) One—
Old Ma Fa fa fa.
All Shh.'
Hazel After *three*, Ma.
Old Ma Sorry, duck.

All concentrate really hard

Hazel Now. One, two, three.
All (*in concentration, joining in*) One, two, three.

> (*singing*) Fa la la la la la fol de rol de ray.

Kernel sings it quite well, but a bit out of tempo. Gypsy sings it with exaggerated feeling, flinging her arms about. Old Ma Coconut just shouts any old thing. The result is ghastly. And all done very seriously.

Hazel Well, that was pretty—

All smile

awful.
Old Ma I think I gave you a few fols what should've been fas, and a few fas what should've been fols.

Hazel Yes. Now, let's try again. *I'll* sing the first line, then you come in and so on. Monkeynut, you play your drum. One, two, three.

                        (*singing*) It's the mer ...

Old Ma (*singing*)

                    Fa la fol dol fa fiddle diddle ...

All Shh.

Gypsy Hazel sings first, Ma, *then* us. Yes?

Old Ma Sorry duck. Fun, ain't it?

Hazel raises her eyes heavenward

Hazel One, two, three

                    (*singing*) It's the merry, merry month of May.

Kernel ⎫ (almost ⎫ (at the same Fa la la la la la fol de rol de ray

Gypsy ⎬ together) ⎨ time)   It's the merry, merry month of

                                     May.

Old Ma ⎭

Hazel (*trying to keep her patience*) No, Ma. You fa la la.

Old Ma What?

Hazel You fa la la.

Old Ma You fa la la yourself. La dee da, you are. So flippin' well fa la la yourself. Ya boo, sucks to you. Ha, ha. (*She crosses her arms in a huff*)

The others are embarrassed

Hazel Oh dear. Now, come on, please. Concentrate.

This time they sing it well, and gradually begin to enjoy it

SONG 8b: **The May Madrigal** (Reprise, contd)

Hazel	It's the merry, merry month of May
Others	Fa la la la la la fol de rol de ray
Hazel	And the summer is on its way
Others	Fa la la la la la fol de rol de ray
Hazel	Now spring is done
	Here comes the sun
Others	Fa la la la la la fol de rol de ray
Hazel	It's the merry, merry month of May
Others	Fa la la la la la fol de rol de ray.

They sing an exuberant 'Fa la la' harmony tag

During this, without being seen by the madrigal singers, William enters downstage and beckons on Professor Jelly

In mime, William points out the Nuts and Professor Jelly exults. He has an idea, and as the madrigal reaches its last line, he visibly does an amazing costume change. In effect he removes his chef-like confectioner garb to reveal a glittering gold lamé-type suit

William takes the confectioner costume off, and stays hidden

Professor Jelly in his new image, strides forward to the singing Nuts, just as they finish and applaud themselves with pleasure

The following scene, up to the exit of Professor Jelly, should be played at considerable speed, so that Hazel signs, having been swept up by a whirlwind of excitement. This also means that the audience will not try to prevent the signing by warning the Nuts that Professor Jelly is the Chocolate Squirter

Jelly Sensational. Fantastic. Amazing. Friends, I mean this very sincerely, if that number is not a chart-bound sound, I am no judge of talent; but I *am* a judge of talent, that is precisely what I am, and my verdict is you shall be taken from this place to appear in my celebrated Talent Show on—Jelly-vision.

Hazel (*excitedly*) Jelly-vision! Is that like television?

Jelly It's in the same mould, yes. Friends, I want to see more of you. The world wants to see more of you. (*He produces, with a flourish, a long scroll-like document*) Sign this contract, sing your madrigal on Jelly-vision, and culture-vultures round the globe will thrill to the sound. Don't delay, sign today. Don't deny the world the chance to applaud this great new group ... (*He thinks*) Yes, I have it—the one and only—Hazel and the Nuts!

The Nuts watch open-mouthed during this virtuous display. Hazel rushes forward and takes the proffered pen

Kernel Hazel!

Old Ma Wotcha doing?

Hazel Signing.

Gypsy (*concerned*) Aye, aye, aye.

Kernel But can't we discuss it?

Hazel Why? What better way to show the world that nuts should be taken seriously than appear on Jelly-vision? It couldn't be better. (*She signs*)

Jelly (*nodding*) It couldn't be better. (*He rubs his hands in glee, and rolls up the Contract*) Friends. The mobile Jelly-vision Studio awaits. Follow me.

Professor Jelly exits happily

Gypsy Oh, Kernel, do we do the right thing?

Kernel (*unsure*) He seemed—enthusiastic.

Old Ma Dead flash, if you ask me.

Monkeynut nods in agreement

Hazel But don't you see—

SONG 9: **We're Gonna be Stars**

During the song, the Nuts get more and more excited, swayed by Hazel's words

> This is it
> This is it
> This is our chance
> The chance to improve

The chance to advance
What better way for us to be seen
Than by millions of viewers on their T.V. screen?

We're gonna be stars
Others   Stars?
Hazel   We're gonna be stars
                Our madrigal will make it
                To number one
All   We're gonna be stars
                Stars
                We're gonna go far
                A new exciting chapter
                For Nuts has begun

We're gonna be stars
Stars
We're gonna be stars
We'll play the biggest theatres
And concert halls
We're gonna be stars
Stars
We're gonna go far
For Hazel and her Nuts
Opportunity calls!

Glamour and fame (Glamour and fame)
Signing our name (Signing our name)
Photo-sessions
Fans, fast cars
Nuts in the news
Press interviews
Gold disc—M.B.E.—
Opening bazaars.

We're gonna be stars
Stars
We're gonna be stars
Our madrigal will make it
To number one
We're gonna be stars
Stars
We're gonna go far
A new exciting chapter
For Nuts has begun.

The music continues as Kernel, Gypsy and Monkeynut go to Old Ma Coconut's pole to help her down

Kernel Stand by, Ma. Down the pole.

Hazel Hang on.

They stop

I think—I don't know quite how to say this, but old Ma's voice is—well ...

Old Ma A bit of an embarrassment, eh duck?

Hazel No, but—it doesn't suit this particular song.

Old Ma My voice never suited *no* song. However particular. Ruined by all the "roll-a-ball-a-bowlin" I've had to belt out all these years.

Hazel Well, if you don't mind ...

Old Ma I'll stop here with pleasure, duck.

Kernel But ...

Gypsy (*worried*) Aye, aye, aye. You *must*-a come with us.

Monkeynut shows concern, too

Old Ma Na. Too much fag sliding down me pole then climbing up again. I'll see you later.

Kernel But—oh dear.

SONG 9: **We're Gonna be Stars** (continued)

Hazel	(*reassuring them*) Glamour and fame Signing our name Photo-sessions Fans, fast cars
All	(*elated again*) Nuts in the news Press interviews Gold disc—M.B.E.— Opening bazaars.

We're gonna be stars
Stars
We're gonna be stars
Our madrigal will make it
To number one
We're gonna be stars
Stars
We're gonna go far
A new exciting chapter
For Nuts has begun
We're gonna be stars
We're gonna be stars
We're gonna be stars.

Hazel, Kernel, Gypsy and Monkeynut exit, taking their drum, etc

Old Ma waves good-bye. If she has to remain on stage, she could pull a curtain to conceal herself. The music changes to the "Here I Come Gathering" theme, as the lighting comes up to daylight

Professor Jelly, still in his lamé suit, and William enter, pulling the caravan

Professor Jelly deftly changes the lettering on the caravan from "JELLY BON-BON" to "JELLY-VISION" by substituting "VISI" for "BON-B". The music changes back to the theme of "We're Gonna be Stars"

Hazel, Kernel, Gypsy and Monkeynut enter, and see the Jelly-vision caravan

The music continues as Professor Jelly steps forward to meet them. William keeps his face hidden. With a flourish, Professor Jelly signals William to reveal the studio.

They revolve the caravan, then Professor Jelly pulls a rope which lifts a canvas roller flap—which is in fact one "side" of the caravan—to reveal a colourful "stage" area inside. Steps lead up to it. Professor Jelly ties off the rope. Professor Jelly politely shows the three singing Nuts up on to the platform— there is just enough room for them to stand comfortably next to each other. There is not enough room for Monkeynut, so he is positioned with his drum, on ground level, to the side of the caravan. William goes off, and re-emerges, at the Professor's command, with the Jelly-vision camera. This has "JELLY-VISION" written on the side, and is enough like a camera to convince Hazel and the others. It has a thick lead attached to it, which leads to a battery pack, which can be strapped to the operator's back. Professor Jelly takes the camera and lines it up on the "stage" area, leaving the battery pack on the ground. Meanwhile, the singing Nuts are adjusting their dress, looking nervous and excited. The music stops

Jelly Stand by, studio. Five seconds to go. Good luck.

The singing Nuts wish each other luck, then stand nervously waiting

Five, four, three ...

In the "silent" final two seconds, Professor Jelly dashes round in front of the camera and smiles a T.V. smile. Somewhere a red light goes on—we are "on the air". A musical "jingle" or "station signal" plays.

Ladies and gentlemen, across the international Jelly-vision network, we proudly present the most extraordinary sound around—Hazel and the Nuts! (*He steps "out of frame" as the Madrigal starts*)

SONG 9: **The May Madrigal** (reprise)

Hazel	It's the merry, merry month of May
Kernel ⎱ **Gypsy** ⎰	Fa la la la la la fol de rol de ray

Gypsy stiffens

Hazel	And the summer is on its way	
Gypsy ⎱ **Kernel** ⎰	A twinge. Danger. Shh. Keep singing.	⎰ speaking ⎱ together

Gypsy ⎤	Fa la la la la la fol de rol de ray
Kernel ⎦	
Hazel	Now spring is done
	Here comes the sun

During the above Professor Jelly returns to behind the camera. Over the last two lines he dramatically presses a lever, and a loud hissing noise is heard over the singing. If possible a "dry ice" smoke effect is used also to suggest that a sort of gas is emitting from the camera

| **Gypsy** ⎤ | Fa la la la la la fol de rol de ray |
| **Kernel** ⎦ | |

Hazel (*beginning to be affected by the "gas", coughing a little, but trying to cover up, aware she is on Jelly-vision*)

It's the merry, merry month of May

| **Gypsy** ⎤ | (*also affected—coughing*) |
| **Kernel** ⎦ | Fa la la la la la fol de rol de ray. |

Musical bridge. The singing Nuts look, concerned, at each other, but are unable to move off the stage. Monkeynut, unaffected on ground level, continues to play his drum, but takes note of his friends' discomfort. Professor Jelly laughs heartily

Jelly It's working! William, come and look. This will teach them to dismiss you.

The singing Nuts are coughing and beginning to stiffen. William emerges, laughing, to see, coming face to face with Monkeynut, who drops his drum in surprise and shock

William Monkeynut. (*He is suddenly ashamed and sobered*)

Pause. They look at each other

I'm ...

Monkeynut, wild-eyed, runs off, terrified

Listen ...

William goes to follow. Monkeynut has gone. William stops and lumbers back

(*filled with guilt*) What have we done?

The singing Nuts sway stiffly

Jelly (*triumphantly*) What have we done? We have successfully applied the glaze to these three splendid specimens. Glazing is one of the secrets of the confectioner's art—look, look at those glazed expressions, it's working wondrously! (*He calls*) Nuts. Can you hear me?

Three glazed nuts (*dazed and zombie-like*) We can hear you.

Jelly You are under my power. What are you?

Three nuts We are under your power.

Jelly We will be proud to be made into superfine, scrumptious choccychocs. Repeat.

Three nuts We will be proud to be made into superfine scrumptious choccy-chocs.

Jelly Now, sing your merry May madrigal while you *may*. (*He laughs*) May. That's rather witty! May it may be, but for you May may not merry be! Sing!

The singing Nuts start singing, with gradually stiffening limbs and glazed faces. The singing is hindered by pinched mouths as they start to "set"

SONG 9: **The May Madrigal** (continued)

Hazel	It's the merry, merry month of May
Kernel ⎫	
Gypsy ⎭	Fa la la la la la fol de rol de ray

Professor Jelly beckons to William and they exit for a moment

Hazel	And the summer is on its way
Kernel ⎫	
Gypsy ⎭	Fa la la la la la fol de rol de ray

Professor Jelly and William return, dragging a large, frightening machine with levers, dials, nozzles, etc.—in large letters on it is written the legend "CHOCOLATE SQUIRTER"

Hazel	Now spring is done
	Here comes the sun
Kernel ⎫	
Gypsy ⎭	Fa la la la la la fol de rol de ray

Jelly (*lining up the machine*) The Chocolate Squirting Machine! Now all we need is fifteen minutes for the glaze to set, and then—the exciting part!

Hazel   It's the merry, merry month of May

This last line is slowed up somewhat, as the glaze has started setting

All   Fa la la la la la

Professor Jelly gleefully takes up the melody. The Nuts stiffen completely and stop singing. William looks worried

Jelly   Fol de rol de ray.

Dramatic music rumble. Professor Jelly cackles, as—

the CURTAIN falls

ACT II

Back at the Fairground area, which is deserted. In fact, all we need to see is the Coconut Shy, so Professor Jelly's caravan could still be on stage, but unlit

Music for tension as Monkeynut runs on breathless and creeps warily along towards the Coconut Shy. He checks no-one has followed him, then looks up at Old Ma Coconut perched on her pole. She is asleep

Monkeynut rushes to the pole and starts to shake it. Then, possibly prompted by the audience, he remembers the correct way to wake a coconut, and grabs two balls lying beneath the pole. He backs away a little, takes aim and throws the balls at Old Ma Coconut and wakes her up

SONG 8: **Roll-a-Ball-a-Bowl-a-Ball** (reprise)

Old Ma   Roll-a-Ball-a-Bowl-a-Ball
               Roll-a-Ball-a-Bowl
               Roll-a-Ball-a-Bowl-a-Ball
               Knock me off me pole.

(*Speaking*) What d'you want?

Monkeynut starts miming that he needs help—and would she please come

Speak up, you nutty ninny. What? (*She peers down*) Oh, it's Monkeynut. All right, duck, don't get in a paddy. What's up?

Monkeynut mimes "Would you come down, please?" The audience may well join in and interpret Monkeynut's mime for Old Ma Coconut. This can naturally be capitalized on if it happens, but I don't think it would be asked for by Old Ma Coconut

What? Me? Down there? Why?

Monkeynut runs on the spot, pointing off—to the caravan

You want to have a race with me?

Monkeynut shakes his head, and does it again

You'll take me somewhere—over there?

Monkeynut nods

What for?

Monkeynut mimes singing a song—big operatic gestures

Directing traffic?

Monkeynut's arms are outstretched

A scarecrow?

Monkeynut shakes his head and points to his mouth opening and shutting

A goldfish?

Monkeynut makes a last attempt

Singing?

Monkeynut nods

Me? That new Hazel nut spurned my singing. The others are singing. On Jelly-vision.

Monkeynut nods—excited. He is making progress. He mimes the glazer being squirted, then does the singing mime again, gradually stiffening

They're nervous?

Monkeynut stiffens completely

Paralysed with fright?

Monkeynut nods

Why?

Monkeynut mimes the glazer again

Someone giving 'em a bit of aggro?

Monkeynut nods

(*To the audience*) *Who's* been giving 'em a bit of aggro?
Audience The Chocolate Squirter.
Old Ma Who?
Audience The Chocolate Squirter.
Old Ma (*with a gasp*) The Chocolate Squirter? Ta. That little squirt again? Right! (*Preparing to leave*) I'll give him what for—I'll give him *more* than what for. Come on, duck, help me down.

Music, as Old Ma Coconut lifts herself up and, with difficulty, slides down the pole, falling on top of Monkeynut, who is trying to lend a hand. This sequence will depend on the design of the pole, and the agility of the performers. It need not be long—just a moment of tangle and funny confusion brought about because of panic. Eventually they hurry towards the caravan, Monkeynut leading the way. The music and lighting change as we return to Professor Jelly's caravan. Kernel, Gypsy and Hazel are completely stiff. The menacing Chocolate Squirting Machine is near the caravan

SONG 10: **Carried Away**

Hazel ⎫	Carried away
Kernel ⎬	We got
Gypsy ⎭	Carried away
	Over-excited
	We blindly went our way
	With danger we flirted

	And now we're gonna get squirted— And carried away.
Gypsy	Carried away To a place we don't know
Kernel	Where one day We will be eaten
Hazel	Carried away Where we don't want to go
Hazel **Kernel** **Gypsy** ⎫ ⎬ ⎭	It really looks as though We are beaten.
	Carried away We got Carried away Over-reacted And now we've got to pay Resigned, disconcerted For soon we're gonna get squirted— And carried away.

At the end of the song, they all heave a big sigh. All speak with difficulty because of the glazing

Hazel Oh, Kernel Walnut, Gypsy Brazil, what can I say?

Kernel (*angrily*) It strikes me you've said quite enough already, Hazel.

Gypsy (*tearfully*) I never want-a to hear you say one word more. If we hadn't listened to you, we ...

Hazel I know. I'm sorry.

Gypsy *You're* sorry!

Kernel Calm down, Gypsy Brazil. Stiff upper lip, eh?

Gypsy Stiff everything. (*She sobs*)

Hazel Listen.

Kernel No. We listened and landed up here.

Hazel I mean, listen—I can hear something.

All listen. Old Ma Coconut and Monkeynut arrive stealthily at the caravan. Monkeynut points to the caravan. They creep up to it, and, without looking to see the Nuts on the stage area, Old Ma knocks on the side, and waits for a reply. The glazed Nuts hear it

Kernel (*whispering*) Who's there?

Old Ma (*whispering*) Me—Old Ma.

Kernel What?

Gypsy (*repeating what she has heard*) Me old ma.

Kernel I thought she was in Brazil.

Gypsy Who?

Kernel Your old ma.

Old Ma Old Ma Coconut and Monkeynut. Rescue service.

Kernel Oh, splendid.

Old Ma Coconut and Monkeynut start to tug at the Nuts' feet and legs to free them

Gypsy Bravo. Bravo.
Old Ma Where's that little squirt, the Squirter?
Kernel He'll be back soon. But watch out. You know who his assistant is, don't you?
Old Ma Who?
Jelly (*off, calling*) William!
Old Ma William?
Kernel Yes.
Jelly (*off*) Come. One minute to squirt-off.

Dramatic chord. Old Ma Coconut realizes the voice is that of the Chocolate Squirter. She and Monkeynut speedily hide behind the caravan—in the nick of time

Professor Jelly and William enter. Professor Jelly has changed back into his confectioner's costume

During the song, Professor Jelly checks and lines up the Chocolate Squirting Machine

SONG 10A: **Here I Come Gathering** (Reprise)

> I'll catch them and squirt them with chocolate
> Then wrap them and box them to sell
> A special selection
> Of high-class confection'ry
> Guaranteed quality, bound to sell well.
>
> So
> Here I come gathering nuts in May ...

(*Speaking*) Stand by for squirt-off count-down. Five, four ... William, be ready to drop the flap after squirting—I want no dust to defile these choice choccies.

William unfastens the rope and holds on to it. Tension music

Three, two ...

At this moment, William is taken completely by surprise by the sight of Monkeynut, who pops out from behind the caravan, waving and smiling

William (*with delighted surprise*) Monkeynut! (*He leaves go of the rope and moves to hug his friend*)

The flap falls in front of the Nuts concealing them from view. Professor Jelly does not notice what has happened

Jelly One!

Old Ma steals from behind the caravan, round and inside, behind the flap

Squirt ...

Professor Jelly looks up and sees what has happened

   (*Furiously*) William! (*Seeing him*) William! (*He advances towards William in fury*)

Monkeynut nips sharply out of the way as William decides to run for it. William dashes round the back of the caravan, followed by Professor Jelly. Immediately Old Ma Coconut pops out, unseen by them, virtually lifting the stiff Gypsy, who assists by hobbling

   Old Ma Coconut and Gypsy exit

Professor Jelly and William reappear from behind the caravan. They chase round the Chocolate Squirting Machine. Professor Jelly catches William

   Gotcha, you botcher.

William struggles, but is subdued by the sheer ferocity of Professor Jelly's verbal attack

     What stupid little game do you think you're playing now, eh? One of your silly jokes? You work for me now, do you understand? Which means perfection. Now—lift the flap. And get it right.

William, stunned, returns to the side of the caravan and pulls the rope, lifting the flap. Professor Jelly returns to the Chocolate Squirting Machine. The raised flap reveals only two Nuts—Kernel and Hazel. William notices, and, scratching his head, counts the Nuts on his fingers a couple of times to make sure

William (*nervously*) Professor, look.

Professor Jelly looks up. William points to one Nut, then two, then shrugs his shoulders

Jelly The brazil's escaped!
William How?
Jelly The glaze must be wearing off. Look!

Sure enough, there are signs of limited movement from Hazel and Kernel—enough to suggest that Gypsy could have escaped under her own steam. Professor Jelly aims the Machine and puts his hand on the lever

     Now, stand by, William. Five, four ... And when we've squirted these two, you get the glazer and we'll grab that brazil back and reglaze it. Three, two ...

William does not listen to this

William What?
Jelly (*gesturing heavenward*) You get the glazer.
William Righto.

   William wanders off to find it, letting the rope go and therefore causing the flap to fall down again

Jelly One.

Old Ma Coconut steals back on and goes inside the caravan

Squirt-off! (*He looks up and sees the flap is down: a cry of rage*) Aaaaaah!
William! (*He rushes to the caravan, and grabs the rope*)

Meanwhile, Old Ma Coconut struggles out of the other end, virtually carrying the glazed Kernel. He helps by hobbling

Old Ma Coconut and Kernel exit

Unaware of this, Professor Jelly pulls the rope, raising the flap, and ties it off. At the same moment, Monkeynut swiftly advances to the Chocolate Squirting Machine, unseen by Professor Jelly, who is concentrating on the flap. Monkeynut pushes the Machine to another part of the stage, and then hides. On the caravan "stage", only Hazel remains: she is moving more freely as the glaze wears off, but cannot move enough to escape

Now ... (*He returns eagerly to where his Chocolate Squirting Machine was. He goes to grab it, but finds it is not there. Perhaps he falls over*) Aaaaaaah! (*He looks up—and with a double-take notices that only one Nut remains*) Aaaaaaaaah! The walnut's escaped!

As Professor Jelly looks around wildly for his machine, William enters, carrying the glazer, wearing the battery pack on his back

William Got it.
Jelly (*sharply*) What?
William Got it. The glazer. Like you said.
Jelly Well, don't just stand there, stupid. After them. The brazil and the walnut. (*Wildly*) Get them back.

William, frightened, nods and exits—the side where the glazed Nuts have escaped, but further downstage

Professor Jelly looks wildly about, sees the Chocolate Squirting Machine where Monkeynut left it, and goes to retrieve it and return it to its former position

Old Ma Coconut creeps back, goes to the caravan, climbs in and grabs Hazel

For the first time the flap is up to allow us—and Professor Jelly—to see her at work. Professor Jelly reacts furiously. He rushes to the caravan, climbs up, and tries to get hold of Old Ma Coconut. But with her large stomach she simply bumps Professor Jelly away, once, then again, and finally a third time very forcefully. This knocks Professor Jelly off the caravan's stage area onto the ground. For a few seconds he is stunned. Old Ma manages to half-lift Hazel from the caravan and start towards the exit. As they reach the exit, Old Ma Coconut and Hazel notice something wrong off; they react to this, turn round, and start heading the other way—back past the caravan

Following them are Gypsy and Kernel, hobbling as fast as they can. They are being chased by William, threatening them with the glazer which slows him down somewhat. Hazel, Old Ma Coconut, Gypsy and Kernel all cross in front of the caravan, chased by William, and exit the other side. They pass the prostrate Professor Jelly, and perhaps even step on him as they go

Professor Jelly manages to stand up just before William reaches him—only to be knocked down by or tangled up with William. By the time they have extricated themselves from this muddle, the escaping Nuts have been given quite a start

William exits in pursuit

Professor Jelly returns to his Chocolate Squirting Machine. Monkeynut creeps out and stands behind it, unseen by Professor Jelly. As Professor Jelly goes to grab it, the machine pulled by Monkeynut appears to mysteriously move away from Professor Jelly's grasp. He reacts. He goes to grab it again. It moves away again. Professor Jelly can't understand it. Then Monkeynut pops out from hiding and waves and makes rude faces in Professor Jelly's direction. Professor Jelly suddenly notices Monkeynut's cheeky behaviour, and, in a terrible fury, slowly and savagely advances towards him. Then develops a short chase around the machine, Professor Jelly and Monkeynut hopping back and forth as in a game of "He"

Monkeynut eventually crawls through Professor Jelly's legs and exits pursued by Professor Jelly. Hazel, Old Ma Coconut, Gypsy and Kernel enter, pursued from one side of the stage across to the other by William. They cross in front of the caravan and exit the other side. Monkeynut enters, pursued by Professor Jelly. They exit the other side. Hazel, Old Ma Coconut, Gypsy and Kernel enter again, pursued by William. They exit the other side. Monkeynut enters again, pursued by Professor Jelly. Monkeynut runs behind the caravan. So does Professor Jelly. They re-emerge the other end of the caravan; Professor Jelly has picked up his nutcrackers from behind. He brandishes them threateningly, and chases the terrified Monkeynut off once more. The first chase returns—William, glazer aimed, following Hazel, Old Ma Coconut, Gypsy and Kernel. William has manoeuvred them in such a way that they run straight up the caravan steps on to the caravan stage area, and are forced to stop there. By the time they realize what has happened, William has nipped round the front and has the glazer trained on them

Tension music increases

Gypsy (*screaming*) Aaaaaah! William! Please, no.

Kernel (*nervously*) Lay down your arms, William, there's a good chap.

William Sorry, Kernel. I have to do as he says. He frightens me. He shouts at me.

Old Ma Then tell him to take a running jump. You're not his kind. You're one of us. A nut.

William I wasn't one of you yesterday. You gave me the big elbow.

Hazel William, that was my fault. I was wrong. I'm sorry. *Please.*

William (*after a pause*) No, I can't. I'm sorry. He frightens me! He shouts at me!

As William's voice rises to a crescendo, he fires the glazer, which emits its

hissing noise and dry-ice-type smoke effect. All four nuts are affected, cough-
ing a little. They start stiffening

    Suddenly the second chase returns—Professor Jelly pursuing Monkeynut,
nutcrackers at the ready

Professor Jelly corners Monkeynut and manages to envelop him in the nut-
crackers. Monkeynut struggles

Jelly Gotcha! I'll teach you not to meddle with me.

William, furious and still holding the glazer, advances

William Professor. Let him go.

Professor Jelly turns in surprise, wheeling round Monkeynut

Jelly You mind your own business.
William One squeeze with those nutcrackers and I'll glaze *you*. (*He points
    it threateningly*)
Jelly Don't be foolish, William. You work for me, remember?
William Let go of my friend.
Jelly I shall not. (*He manhandles Monkeynut roughly in the nutcrackers*)
William All right. Five seconds to glaze. Five—four ...

He speaks deliberately, and the audience will probably join in the countdown

    Three—two ...

Professor Jelly, realizing William means business, looks wildly about

    One.
Jelly Very well. You win. (*He lets Monkeynut go*)

Monkeynut rushes to William's side

    But you'll regret it.

William still keeps the glazer trained on Professor Jelly

William I don't see why.
Jelly You wait. I'll make you slave for me.
William Wrong. I'm not lifting another finger for you. I should never have
    lifted a finger for you in the first place. You can clear off. (*He advances*)
    Go on. Scram.

Professor Jelly, naturally scared by the glazer, backs away

Jelly You'll be useless without me. You're useless anyway. Even the Fair
    sacked you.
William They'll take me back after I've rescued them.

He briefly indicates the four Nuts, who are now very stiff

Jelly Rescued them, William? You'll never rescue them. The glaze is nearly
    set—even stronger than the first time. And before it has time to wear off,
    I'll be back—(*he makes a leap and grabs the Chocolate Squirting
    Machine*)—to finish them off! With this!

Professor Jelly pushes the Machine and exits, cackling

William Come on, Monkeynut. Let's get to work.

William removes the glazer, puts it down and then they both dash to the caravan, and, climbing on the "stage" area, start trying to remove the glazed Nuts. But all are solidly stuck to the floor. William and Monkeynut try a few heaves, but without success

It's no good. The Professor was right. The second glaze is stronger. It's a problem.

Kernel (*through pinched lips*) You'll have to crack it.

William (*turning to him*) I know, Kernel. We're trying to crack the problem right now.

Kernel No, no. Not crack the problem—crack the glaze, crack the glaze.

William Crack the glaze. How?

Old Ma (*with an effort*) Make us laugh, duck. Make us roar with laughter. That'll crack it.

William Laugh. Right. Er—I'll tell you a joke. Er—I know. What do you call a conker with a sore throat?

The Nuts (*with pinched voices*) We don't know. What do you call a conker with a sore throat?

William A hoarse chestnut. Ha, ha, ha.

No reaction from the glazed Nuts

No? Well, I suppose it wasn't that funny. How else can I make them laugh?

Pause

I know. Tickling. We'll try giving you a tickle.

Monkeynut and William both tickle the glazed nuts in all the obvious ticklish spots

Ticky ticky ticky tick. Ticky ticky ticky tick. Ticky ticky ticky tick.

No reaction

Oh, it's no good. The tickle doesn't get through the glaze.

There is a loud scream from Gypsy. William turns

Is it working?

Gypsy (*with pinched mouth*) No. A twinge. A twinge.

Kernel What do you see?

Gypsy Aye, aye, aye. I see—help—from lots of people—something to do with—our May Madrigal ...

Hazel (*excited though glazed*) I know. Listen.

Kernel We're not listening to you any more.

Hazel Please. I know this is all my fault and you have no reason to trust me, but *please* listen.

Pause

Old Ma Can't do no 'arm, duck. Listening.

Kernel Oh very well. Fire ahead.

Hazel Thank you. It's the "lots of people" Gypsy Brazil sees. I think they've come to hear us sing the May Madrigal. I wrote that poster, remember? They're here. Look.

William and Monkeynut turn towards the audience, and jump with surprise at the sight of them

William (*with a gasp, whispering*) You're right. They're all sitting there. Waiting.

Hazel (*whispering*) Say you're sorry, the madrigal is delayed. Then ask them to help us.

William (*whispering*) Now?

Hazel (*whispering*) Of course. The Chocolate Squirter will be back any moment.

William Right. (*He coughs nervously, as though addressing an audience for the first time. To the audience*) Ladies and Gents. Er—

Hazel (*prompting, whispering*) Sorry.

William (*whispering*) What?

Hazel (*prompting*) Sorry.

William (*whispering*) That's all right.

Hazel No, say sorry to *them*.

William (*loudly*) Sorry to *them*.

Hazel No. Don't be stupid.

William (*to the audience loudly*) No. Don't be stupid.

Hazel (*whispering deliberately*) Will—you—help—us?

William (*to Hazel crossly*) What do you *think* I'm doing? I'm *trying* to help you.

Hazel (*trying to keep her patience*) No. Ask the audience. Will—

William (*to the audience*) Will—

Hazel —you—

William —you—

Hazel —help—

William —help—

Hazel —us?

William —us?

He gives the last word an upward inflection, to ensure an answer from the audience. If necessary he can repeat the whole question

Audience Yes.

William Will you?

Audience Yes.

William Thank you. Now, how can they help?

Old Ma They've got to make us split our sides laughing. Split the glaze anyway.

William Right. I know. (*to the audience*) Everyone think of something really nutty and silly to do—something to make 'em laugh. A funny face, or a funny movement, or a funny noise—the nuttiest thing you can think of. Make 'em really laugh till they burst the glaze! One, two—er—*go*!

Music, as William and Monkeynut encourage the audience to do their nutty things. After a while the four glazed nuts start finding it funny. They start laughing and gradually shaking and moving and "bursting" out of the glaze

It's working! Come on!

Monkeynut and William keep the audience going, until the arms and legs of the glazed nuts start stretching out, and it is clear the plan has worked

Thank you.

Hazel is the first to get free. She is helped down by William

Hazel Thank you, William. (*to the audience*) Thank you, everybody.

SONG 11: **Nuttiness is Best**

During the song the other glazed Nuts are released and helped from the caravan

> I was wrong, I was wrong
> Suddenly I see
> If it hadn't been for nuttiness
> We wouldn't be free—
>
> Nutty, nutty, nutty, nutty, nuttiness
> Nutty, nutty, nutty,
> Nuttiness is best.
>
> Nutty, nutty, nutty, nutty, nuttiness
> Nutty, nutty, nutty,
> Nuttiness is best.
>
> If we'd done something clever
> We'd have never
> Got away
> When put to the test
> Nuttiness is best.
>
> Instead of something brainy
> Something zany
> Won the day
> When put to the test
> Nuttiness is best.
>
> All the knowledge I possess
> Would have served us less
> Than the nutty plan
> That did the trick—
>
> In such a situation
> Education

Didn't pay
When put to the test
Nuttiness is best.

By now the other three Nuts are all freed

All   Nutty, nutty, nutty, nutty, nuttiness
Nutty, nutty, nutty,
Nuttiness is best.

Nutty, nutty, nutty, nutty, nuttiness
Nutty, nutty, nutty,
Nuttiness is best.

If we'd done something clever
We'd have never
Got away
When put to the test
Nuttiness is best.

Instead of something brainy
Something zany
Won the day
When put to the test
Nuttiness is best.

Hazel   All the knowledge I possess
All   Would have served us less
Than the nutty plan
That did the trick.

You'll be a fuddy-duddy
With all study
And no play
When put to the test
Nuttiness is best.

Nutty, nutty, nutty, nutty, nuttiness
Nutty, nutty, nutty,
Nuttiness is best.

Nutty, nutty, nutty, nutty, nuttiness
Nutty, nutty, nutty,
Nuttiness is best.

Nutty, nutty, nutty, nutty, nuttiness
Nutty, nutty, nutty,
Nuttiness is best.

By the end of the song all six Nuts are downstage, free and dancing happily

Gypsy (*suddenly*) Aaaaaah! A twinge.

Pause. All look at her in rapt anticipation

The Chocolate Squirter's coming!

All panic, then make their escape into the audience. They leave the glazer behind

Kernel Can we hide down here, please?
All Don't tell him we're here. Please! etc., etc.

As quickly as possible they hide amongst the audience, crouching behind seats, using children as a screen. Music for tension

> *Suddenly, with an excited cackle, Professor Jelly enters with the Chocolate Squirting Machine. Chortling merrily, without bothering to check that the glazed nuts are where he left them, he lines up the machine, checks its lever, etc., then speaks gleefully*

Jelly Five seconds to squirt-off. Five, four—(*he looks up at the caravan "stage" area for the first time*)—three, two ... (*He does an enormous double-take, sees the "stage" is empty, and the "one" of his countdown changes into a cry of rage*) Waaaaaah! I don't believe it! (*To himself*) Where are they? Where are they? (*Muttering angrily, he paces up and down*) Such beautiful unblemished specimens. With them I could have created choccychocs fit for royalty! A princess might have nibbled my walnut whirl ... (*Suddenly he stops. He has seen the audience, and reacts as if he had no idea they were there. To himself*) People. Sitting waiting. (*He looks from the audience to the caravan and back again*) They must have witnessed the escape. (*He coughs, then puts on all his charm as he addresses the audience*) Er—excuse me, Ladies, Gentlemen, young ladies, young gentlemen. Have you by any chance seen a small cluster of nuts recently?
Audience No.
Jelly Fairly common sort of nuts. A walnut, a hazel, a brazil, a coconut ... you haven't seen them?
Audience No.
Jelly (*getting rattled, losing his charming gloss*) But you *must* have. They were over there. (*He points to the caravan*). But moments ago ... (*He stops and has a thought*) Wait! (*insidiously*) You know more about this than meets the iris. You helped them to escape. (*sharply*) Didn't you?
Audience No.
Jelly You wouldn't lie to me, would you?
Audience No.
Jelly Do you deny that I am not correct in stating that you didn't help them?

This question is so confusing, it should lead to a less confident reply—"Yes" and "No" and a stunned silence could be the response

Ah! You're not sure! Gotcha! That proves it. You helped them escape. And you know where they are now. Don't you?
Audience No.
Jelly Oh yes you do.
Audience Oh no we don't.

Jelly Oh yes you do.
Audience Oh no we don't.
Jelly Do.
Audience Don't.
Jelly Do.
Audience Don't.

Pause. Professor Jelly looks suspiciously at the Audience

Jelly Very well. (*He has a sudden idea. He produces a box or bag of confectionery, and puts on all the oozing charm again*) If you tell me where the Nuts are, I'll give you a sweetie. (*He goes down to the audience to bribe them*) Who fancies one, eh? You do? You? All I want is a little information in return. That's fair, isn't it? Mmm? Anyone else? How could you refuse one of these delicious delicacies? Lemon and liquorice pastilles, greengage gobstoppers. Just tell me where the Nuts are, and you can have as many as you wish. Well, are you going to tell me?

The above speech may have to be improvised slightly from performance to performance. The likelihood is that the children in the audience will refuse to be bribed

Audience No.

Eventually Professor Jelly has to give up

Jelly (*snarling*) My, you loathsome little goody-goodies. You incorruptible scum! You'll regret this. What's a handful of silly nuts to you? They're my livelihood! Without them I'll starve! All thanks to a clutch of chivalrous children. You'll pay, you'll see. (*He thinks, then suddenly has an idea. He giggles, nastily. This builds to a manic laugh*) I've got it! The greatest novelty in the history of confectionery since jelly babies—CHOCOLATE CHILDREN!

SONG 12: **Chocolate Children**

> Chocolate Children
> Chocolate Children
> What a sensation
> What an inspiration
> Chocolate Children
> What a caper
> Chocolate Children
> Wrapped in silver paper
> Oh what a sweet
> What a treat
> They'll be
> Chocolate Children
> Hee, hee, hee!
>
> Chocolate Children
> Chocolate Children

Gooey and munchy
Crackly and crunchy
Kiddies assortment
Son or daughter
Chocolate Children
Twenty P. a quarter
Oh what a sweet
What a treat
They are
Chocolate Children
Ha, ha, ha!

With what affection
And hate
This new confection
I'll create
I can't wait
To see my customers' eyes
When they see my latest
Positively greatest
Lipsmacking chocolate surprise.

Chocolate Children
Chocolate Children
What a sensation
What an inspiration
Chocolate Children
What a caper
Chocolate children
Wrapped in silver paper
Coated in choc—
—'late from top
To toe
Chocolate Children
Ho, ho, ho.

Ho, ho, ho,
Ha, ha, ha,
Hee, hee, hee
Chocolate Children
Made by me!

At the end of the song, Professor Jelly starts "counting" the audience

Mmm. I shall have to prepare for such a mammoth operation. (*To the audience*) You have two minutes in which to get ready to be glazed—(*he fondly strokes the glazer*)—then squirted. Chocolate children! I'll make my fortune. No more will I need nuts!

Laughing, Professor Jelly pushes off the Chocolate Squirting Machine, also carrying the glazer which William left on the ground

All the six Nuts in amongst the audience stand up and, during the following conversation, gather either on stage or in a visible part of the auditorium

William (*to the audience*) Oh well done. You've saved us!

Kernel Quiet, William. They've bravely got us out of danger, but now they're in danger themselves.

Old Ma They helped us. Now we'd better help *them*.

Hazel Yes, but how?

Gypsy Aaaaaah! A twinge! A twinge!

They all gather round her

Kernel What do you see?

Gypsy Aye, aye, aye. See—a plan! A plan to fool the Chocolate Squirter and give him a taste of his-a own medicine. (*eyes closed, concentrating*) Everybody—(*indicating the audience*)—must pretend to be glazed. Stay still and stiff. Make the Chocolate Squirter really think they *are* glazed.

Old Ma Yeah, but what's to stop 'em really *being* glazed?

Gypsy William. Something to do with William.

William I know. Look, I know how the glazer works. I'll sabotage it. Pull the lead from the battery pack when he's not looking. Then it won't work.

Kernel But he'll know. If it's not working, it won't make that hissing noise.

Hazel Everybody can make the hissing noise. That will fool him.

Kernel Yes, good. Then what?

Gypsy Then he will fetch the Chocolate Squirting Machine and start the count-down to squirt-off—suddenly everybody makes a lot of noise and takes him by surprise, and—

William —and then we *squirt* him!

Gypsy Yes.

Old Ma But what sort of noise can they make?

Kernel Well, there's the May Madrigal—that's what they came to hear.

William I've never sung it.

Old Ma And I wasn't allowed to sing it.

Gypsy And *we* were glazed when we did sing it.

Hazel We need a song we *all* know.... I've got it—the "Nutty Song". (*She starts singing*) Nutty, nutty, nutty, nutty, nuttiness ...

Kernal Splendid. Let's get organized. Have a practice.

Old Ma Hang on. If the Nutty Song's not enough to surprise him, why don't I get all the balls from the coconut shy, and we can all chuck 'em at him.

Kernel Excellent wheeze. Quick as you can, Ma.

Old Ma dashes off to the Coconut Shy

Now, let's plan the campaign in detail. Monkeynut, you pretend to be the Chocolate Squirter.

Monkeynut acts out the plan as it is described

William is hidden—(*he has an idea*)—behind the caravan.

William goes there

The Chocolate Squirter comes back, glazer at the ready. William creeps out during countdown. Removes the lead.

William mimes all this

On zero—(*taking in the audience*)—everyone hiss—come on, let's hear you!

The audience hisses

Splendid. Now you start pretending to be affected by the glaze. Cough a bit. Good. And now start stiffening—like you saw us stiffening. And glazed eyes.

All the nuts mime the stiffening too, to help the audience

Excellent. Now completely stiff. As if the glaze has set.

Pause, to let the audience "freeze"

Gypsy (*now out of her trance*) Bravo, bravo. Kernel Walnut, I have-a thought of something.

Kernel Fire ahead.

Gypsy When we were glazed, the Chocolate Squirter asked us questions to check that we *were* glazed. Maybe everyone should be prepared for such-a questions.

Kernel Indeed, yes! Now what did he ask?

Gypsy Can you hear me?

Kernel Yes. Perfectly. Now what was the first question?

Gypsy Caramba. No. That was it. "Can you hear me?"

Kernel Oh yes. And everyone answers. "We can hear you"—all right, everyone, after three. One, two, three.

Audience We can hear you.

William Yeah. But it needs to be all glazed—with stiff lips. Like this. (*He demonstrates*) We can hear you.

Kernel Good. Come on, everyone.

Audience We can hear you.

Gypsy (*impersonating Professor Jelly*) You are under my power. What are you?

Kernel Come on.

Audience We are under your power.

Gypsy (*impersonating Professor Jelly*) We will be proud to be made into superfine, scrumptious choccy-chocs. Repeat.

Audience (*led by Kernel Walnut*) We will be proud to be made into superfine, scrumptious choccy-chocs.

Kernel First class. Now then, the Chocolate Squirter is satisfied you are really glazed. He takes the Chocolate Squirting Machine—

Monkeynut mimes this

points it at you. And starts count-down to squirt-off.

Gypsy Five, four, three, two—

Kernel And on the cry of—

Gypsy —one—
Kernel —everyone sings the Nutty Song.
William Can I teach it to them?
Kernel Yes, please.
William (*to the audience*) Right. It goes—er ...

> Nutty, nutty, nutty, nutty, nuttiness
> Nutty, nutty, nutty,
> Nuttiness is best.

William teaches the audience the song; in two sections is probably the simplest way

SONG 12A: **Nuttiness is Best** (Reprise)

William ⎫   Nutty, nutty, nutty, nutty, nuttiness
Audience ⎰   Nutty, nutty, nutty,
Nuttiness is best.

They sing it a couple of times, as necessary. Before the final practice, William has another idea

William Hey, I've got a great idea. This time we'll sing it twice through, very loud, and why doesn't everyone stand up and wave your arms in the air while you're singing? That would really frighten him!

William and the audience rehearse with the movements

Gypsy Bravo! Bravo! When it is really loud, it will take him by surprise for certain.
William And then I'll nip out and finish him off!
Kernel Absolutely. Now, better just run over everything once more if you don't mind.

Everyone mimes or acts his part, encouraging the audience to participate at the relevant moments

Everyone in position? Ready, steady, go.

Monkeynut "enters" as Professor Jelly

Chocolate Squirter arrives. Aims glazer.

William creeps out and mimes removing the lead from the battery pack

Gypsy (*doing Professor Jelly's voice*) Five, four, three, two, one, zero ...
Kernel Hiss. Sssssssssssss.

The audience hisses

Now, pretend the glaze is working. Coughs. Stiffen. Good. Now *very still.*
Gypsy (*impersonating Professor Jelly*) Can you hear me?

Monkeynut mimes the words

Audience (*led, if necessary, by Kernel*) We can hear you.
Gypsy You are under my power. What are you?

Audience We are under your power.

Gypsy We will be proud to be made into superfine scrumptious choccy-chocs. Repeat.

Audience We will be proud to be made into superfine, scrumptious choccy-chocs.

Kernel Good. Now he gets the machine.

Monkeynut mimes this, points it at the audience

Gypsy Five, four, three, two, ONE ...

William pops out to lead the Nutty Song, encouraging the audience to stand and wave their arms

SONG 12A: **Nuttiness is Best** (continued)

During this chorus, Monkeynut reacts shocked and surprised, backing away

Audience   Nutty, nutty, nutty, nutty, nuttiness
                      Nutty, nutty, nutty
                      Nuttiness is best.

                      Nutty, nutty, nutty, nutty, nuttiness
                      Nutty, nutty, nutty
                      Nuttiness is best.

William Then out I pop, and Bob's your uncle!

Old Ma Coconut enters with a basket of balls

Old Ma And here's your ma! Got the balls.

All cheer excitedly at the plan's successful rehearsal. Suddenly they freeze

Jelly (*off, singing*) Here I come gathering children in May
                        Children in May ...

Kernel He's coming.

All take a couple of balls each and start scuttling to their places

          Good luck, everybody!

The Nuts without specific jobs on stage go into the audience again, including Old Ma Coconut

Professor Jelly enters, gleefully pushing his Chocolate Squirting Machine. The glazer is balanced on top. He is already wearing the battery pack on his back

Jelly (*singing under his breath*) Chocolate children, chocolate children ...
(*He takes up the glazer. To the audience*) May this teach you not to meddle in matters that don't concern you. Stand by. *Good*-bye. Ha ha. Five, four, three—(*he trains the glazer on the audience*)

William creeps out of hiding and successfully removes the lead from the battery pack without Professor Jelly noticing. He does a big thumbs-up sign to the audience

          —two, one, zero.

The audience hiss as rehearsed. If necessary, Kernel, in the auditorium, can whisper instructions. The audience begins coughing, stiffening, etc.

Lovely, lovely!

Eventually the audience is still, apparently set

Now, listen to me, children. Can you hear me?
Audience We can hear you.
Jelly You are under my power. What are you?
Audience We are under your power.
Jelly We will be proud to be made into superfine, scrumptious choccychocs. Repeat.
Audience We will be proud to be made into superfine, scrumptious choccy-chocs.
Jelly Lovely, lovely!

Tension music

Count-down to squirt-off. (*He aims the Chocolate Squirting Machine at the audience*) Five, four, three, two, ONE ...

William pops out of hiding and leads the audience in a really loud version of the Nutty Song

SONG 12A: **Nuttiness is Best** (continued)

Audience   Nutty, nutty, nutty, nutty, nuttiness
                          Nutty, nutty, nutty
                          Nuttiness is best.

                          Nutty, nutty, nutty, nutty, nuttiness
                          Nutty, nutty, nutty,
                          Nuttiness is best.

Professor Jelly is taken off his guard. He reacts amazed, shocked and backs away a little, leaving go of the Machine

Jelly You dastardly, damnable—double-crossers! You wait. I'll ...
Old Ma Fire, everybody, fire!

The balls are flung at Professor Jelly, who is knocked backwards, away from the Machine. At the appropriate moment, William steps in, grabs the Machine and trains it on Professor Jelly, who suddenly sees it

Jelly No! No! Help! No!

William backs him up to the caravan

William Five, four, three—

By this time the audience should be joining in, plus the other Nuts, who return from the audience

All —two, one—Squirt-off!!

At the last moment Professor Jelly dashes behind *the caravan. William presses the lever, aiming it behind the caravan from the other side. Frightening sound of the "squirt". No chocolate need actually be squirted as it happens out of vision. Music*

The Nuts swiftly wheel off the caravan, revealing a chocolate covered statue of Professor Jelly. The real Professor Jelly exits behind the caravan as it is wheeled off. All the Nuts rush back, jumping for joy, laughing at the Chocolate Man, clearing away the glazer, and the Chocolate Squirting Machine

All the Nuts (*to the audience*) Bravo, well done, you did it, you fooled him, etc.

William becomes slightly separated from the others. He looks on at this indulgent scene of self-congratulation

Kernel Splendid team effort! Gypsy Brazil's twinge starting us off, Old Ma Coconut's idea to shoot balls at him—even Hazel and her Nutty Song. Splendid.

Old Ma And you, Kernel, you put it all together and made it work.

Kernel Oh. Thank you. Yes.

William turns and starts to exit. Monkeynut notices and taps Kernel on the shoulder, drawing his attention to it

(*misunderstanding at first*) Oh, yes. You, too, Monkeynut, well done. What? Oh ... (*seeing William despondently leaving*) William. (*He calls*) William. I didn't mean to leave you out. You did more than any of us.

William (*a huge beam spreading across his face*) Really?

Kernel Yes. And we would be honoured if you would return to the Fair to work with us.

William Well—

Monkeynut hugs him

—yes, please!

All applaud

Kernel I should never have dismissed you. I apologize.

Hazel So do I, William. I apologize to everyone for trying to—well, change you. When none of you need changing one bit.

Gypsy You go back home now, yes? To the school? To learn more?

Hazel Yes, but I've learned a lot from you, too.

Kernel We've all learned a lot—though the lesson nearly ended in disaster. And, you know, Hazel, all you said about gaining respect—er, nuts by name, not nuts by nature, well, I fancy some people might say we've succeeded a little ...

Old Ma (*pointing to the audience*) That lot for a start! If it weren't for our nutty plan, they'd all be chocolate children by now!

Gypsy Aaaaaah. A twinge. A twinge.

All gather round

Kernel What do you see? What has the future in store?

Gypsy Aye, aye, aye. I see—us—celebrating! Safe. At the Nutty May Fair!

All cheer

SONG 12B: **Come to the Nutty May Fair/Nuttiness is Best/The May Madrigal** (Reprise)

During the song the set changes back to the Nutty May Fair

All   Heigh-ho, come to the Nutty May Fair
                       Heigh-ho, roll up for fun and fresh air
                       We've stalls and we've sideshows
                       Games you can play
                       So come try your luck now
                       Just step up this way
                       Ev'ry Nut who is any Nut's bound to be there
                       So come to the Nutty May Fair
                       Come to the Nutty May Fair.

                       Surprises
                       Prizes
                       Lots to do and see
                       Thrills
                       Spills
                       Ooohs and aaahs and wheeeeeee!

All exit except Hazel and Monkeynut

Hazel   (*singing to Monkeynut*)
                       I was wrong, I was wrong
                       Suddenly I see
                       If it hadn't been for nuttiness
                       We wouldn't be free.

The others come on again, with coloured ribbons

All   Nutty, nutty, nutty, nutty, nuttiness
                       Nutty, nutty, nutty,
                       Nuttiness is best.

                       Nutty, nutty, nutty, nutty, nuttiness
                       Nutty, nutty, nutty,
                       Nuttiness is best.

                       If we'd done something clever
                       We'd have never
                       Got away
                       When put to the test
                       Nuttiness is best.

                       Instead of something brainy
                       Something zany
                       Won the day
                       When put to the test
                       Nuttiness is best.

Hazel   All the knowledge I possess
                   Would have served us less
                   Than the nutty plan
                   That did the trick.

All   You'll be a fuddy-duddy
                   With all study
                   And no play
                   When put to the test
                   Nuttiness is best.

*During the next section, the Nuts attach coloured ribbons to the Chocolate
Man, and dance round him as though he is a maypole; also wrapping him up,
like a sweet, in the ribbons*

                   It's the merry, merry month of May
                   Fa la la la la la fol de rol de ray
                   And the summer is on its way
                   Fa la la la la la fol de rol de ray
                   Now spring is done
                   Here comes the sun
                   Fa la la la la la fol de rol de ray
                   It's the merry, merry month of May
                   Fa la la la la la fol de rol de ray.

                   (*Harmony "Fa la la" section*)

                   Nutty, nutty, nutty nutty, nuttiness
                   Nutty, nutty, nutty
                   Nuttiness is best.

                   Nutty, nutty, nutty, nutty, nuttiness
                   Nutty, nutty, nutty
                   Nuttiness is best.

                   Nutty, nutty, nutty, nutty
                   Nutty, nutty, nutty, nutty
                   Nutty, nutty, nutty, nutty
                   Nuttiness is best.

                              CURTAIN

FURNITURE AND PROPERTY LIST

ACT I

On stage: Fortune-telling tent
Monkeynut's cage
Coconut shy behind canvas awning. *Around base:* balls (N.B. If possible this should be off stage when not in use)
Boxing-booth. *In it:* nut-case
Trolley with rattle, whistles, drums, handbell, cymbals, horn, hooter, other noise-making devices, towel
Earth mound

Tea stall (optional)
Ice cream stall (optional)
"Nutty-Go-Round" (optional)
"Cashew Desk" (optional)
"Nutty Dip" (optional)
Soap box (optional)

Off stage: Trick steel bar (**Monkeynut**)
Trick weight (**Kernel, Monkeynut**)
"Jelly Bon-bon" caravan. *In it:* samples of sweets in tray or basket, huge nutcrackers, roller flap to reveal T.V. studio stage, red light (**Professor Jelly**)
3 lanterns (**Kernel, Gypsy, Hazel**)
Banner (**Hazel**)
Long scroll, pen (**Professor Jelly**)
Glazer (T.V. camera) with thick lead (**William**)
Battery pack with strap (**William**)
"Chocolate Squirting" machine (**Professor Jelly, William**)

Personal: **Gypsy**: crystal nut
Kernel: whip
William: boxing gloves

ACT II

Strike: All booths except Coconut Shy and Caravan
Trolley and contents
All props except balls

Set: "Chocolate Squirter" near Caravan
Glazed chocolate statue of Professor Jelly concealed behind Caravan
Off stage: Box or bag of confectionery (**Professor Jelly**)
Coloured ribbons (**Nuts**)

LIGHTING PLOT

Property fittings required: nil
Exterior. A clearing with Fair booths

ACT I

To open:	House Lights up	
Cue 1	As action starts *Fade House Lights, bring up general lighting to dawn* *effect: increase gradually to daylight*	(Page 1)
Cue 2	**Gypsy** has a "twinge" *Lights flash up and down* (optional)	(Page 4)
Cue 3	**Gypsy** has a "twinge" *Lights flash up and down* (optional)	(Page 10)
Cue 4	**Monkeynut** exits after **William** *Cross-fade to caravan lighting*	(Page 12)
Cue 5	**Professor Jelly** and **William** exit with caravan *Cross-fade to fairground lighting—night*	(Page 17)
Cue 6	**Gypsy** has a "twinge" *Lights flash up and down* (optional)	(Page 19)
Cue 7	**All:** "We're gonna be stars"—general exit *Cross-fade to daylight, concentrating on caravan*	(Page 28)
Cue 8	**Gypsy** has a "twinge" *Lights flash up and down* (optional)	(Page 29)

ACT II

To open:	Dim lighting, concentrating on coconut shy	
Cue 9	**Monkeynut** and **Old Ma** move to caravan *Bring up general lighting, favouring caravan*	(Page 33)
Cue 10	**Gypsy** has a "twinge" *Lights flash up and down* (optional)	(Page 44)
Cue 11	**Gypsy** has a "twinge" *Lights flash up and down* (optional)	(Page 43)
Cue 12	**Gypsy** has a "twinge" *Lights flash up and down* (optional)	(Page 47)
Cue 13	**Nuts** wheel off caravan All lighting up to full	(Page 52)
Cue 14	**Gypsy** has a "twinge" *Lights flash up and down* (optional)	(Page 52)

EFFECTS PLOT

ACT I

Cue 1   **Professor Jelly** pushes camera lever   (Page 30)
Loud hissing noise

ACT II

Cue 2   **William** fires glazer   (Page 38)
Hissing noise

Cue 3   **William** fires Squirter behind caravan   (Page 51)
"Frightening sound"

INCIDENTAL MUSIC PLOT

ACT I

Cue 1   **Kernel:** "... for fun and fresh air"   (Page 2)
Dramatic rumble

Cue 2   **Kernel:** "... nuts that are rare"   (Page 3)
Dramatic rumble

Cue 3   **Gypsy** gazes into crystal nut   (Page 4)
Tension music, earthquake rumble

Cue 4   **William** prepares to lift weight   (Page 7)
Dramatic rumble

Cue 5   **Professor Jelly** picks up scent   (Page 13)
Tension music

Cue 6   **Professor Jelly** hides nutcrackers   (Page 14)
Dramatic rumble

Cue 7   **William** experiments with nutcrackers   (Page 16)
Tension music

Cue 8   **Professor Jelly:** "... you will perform better"   (Page 17)
Tension music

Cue 9   **Kernel:** "What do you see"   (Page 19)
Tension music

Cue 10   **Monkeynut** flings himself into **Kernel**'s arms   (Page 20)
Dramatic chord

Cue 11   **Kernel:** "... the Chocolate Squirter"   (Page 20)
Dramatic chord

Cue 12   **Professor Jelly:** "Fol de Rol de Ray"   (Page 31)
Dramatic rumble

ACT II

Printed in Great Britain by Butler & Tanner Ltd, Frome and London